Lakeland
Bobbin Makers

The Philipson Mills
Cunsey to Spark Bridge

Douglas Philipson

HANDSTAND
PRESS

HANDSTAND PRESS

Published by Handstand Press
East Banks, Dent, Sedbergh, Cumbria. England
LA10 5QT

First published in 2010

© Gillian Philipson-Heinrichs

Editor: Liz Nuttall, Handstand Press
Designed and set by Long House Publishing Services,
Broughton Mills, Cumbria
Printed in Great Britain by CPI Antony Rowe, Chippenham, Wilts.

ISBN: 978-0-9552009-60

*Front Cover (clockwise, from top right): Bobbin tops; interior, Spark Bridge Bobbin Mill;
sample room, Spark Bridge Bobbin Mill; Coppice stack, Spark Bridge Bobbin Mill
(Courtesy of the Philipson family);
Back Cover: A 1930's View of Spark Bridge and the Bobbin Mill
(Courtesy of the Philipson family)*

Acknowledgements

Grateful thanks to all those who encouraged the publication of this book and supplied valuable information, photographic and documentary material. Special mention to Eileen Thompson who worked at Spark Bridge Mill for many years until its closure in 1983. Thanks also to Irvine Hunt, Helen Caldwell from the Cumbria Industrial History Society, Kendal Museum of Lakeland Life, The Stott Park Bobbin Mill, Barrow Record Office and Local Studies Library, John Garratt, Mrs Anne Bigland, Dr Sherilyn MacGregor, Dr Simon Pardoe, Roger Newbold, Eleanor Alcock and Kate Kirkwood.

Contents

Douglas Philipson as a young man (*Courtesy of the Philipson family*)

Preface

This is the story of my father, Douglas Philipson (1915-2000), who was raised at The Strands, about a mile and a half from Spark Bridge on the River Crake in what was then, the county of Lancashire. As a young boy he went to work for William Philipson, his uncle, at Spark Bridge Bobbin Mill, where he remained in employment until 1956, with a break during the Second World War. He received no special favours as a family member, in fact, quite the opposite. He worked long hours for low wages and travelled back and forth from the mill on his bicycle in all kinds of weather. He learned every aspect of bobbin making and gained a life-long love of working with wood.

Management of the mill passed from William Philipson to Douglas's father Charles in the late 1930s. In 1940 Douglas married Catherine Marshall from Dollar in Scotland and they moved into The Nook, next door to The Strands. When he returned from the War in 1945 he went back to work at the mill but the business was in decline. The arrival of plastics had made wooden bobbins obsolete and the Lancashire cotton industry was shrinking rapidly. The writing was on the wall. Charles Philipson died in 1955 and Douglas's brother, Charles Stuart who had emigrated to Canada, persuaded my father to join him in Ottawa. So Douglas, Catherine and their three daughters, Gillian, Roseanne and Moira moved to Canada in April 1956. The Spark Bridge Mill was sold to the firm of J. E. Borell.

As a hobby in mid and later life my father made beautiful pine furniture for family and friends, often working from a simple sketch on a scrap of paper. Over time he acquired the skills of a fine cabinet maker, customizing anything from beds to china cabinets and entertainment units. In particular, his finishing techniques using the pine of his adopted country, was especially beautiful. He has left a wonderful legacy for his family, of tables, chairs, beds and other furniture, crafted in honey hued pine.

Douglas Philipson was concerned that there was little documentation regarding the manufacture and business operation of wood bobbin making in Great Britain, in 1980. When he retired from his job, in Canada, as production manager in a cosmetics factory, he decided to write his own account of the trade and his family connection with it. The publication of this book is the result of resurrecting the notes found in an old folder after his death. Hopefully it will provide a useful history of wooden bobbin manufacture in south Lakeland and an insight into the life of a working mill during its heyday in the first half of the twentieth century.

This book is dedicated to my father, Douglas Philipson.

Gillian Philipson-Heinrichs
Ottawa, Canada, 2010

Map of South Lakeland, showing bobbin mills associated with the Philipson family between 1800 and 1956. (© *Roger Newbold*)

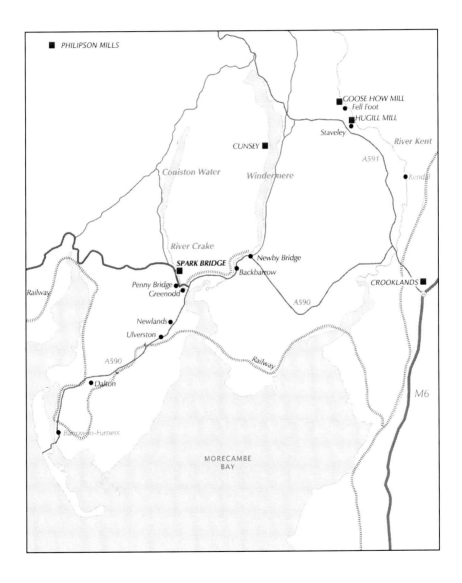

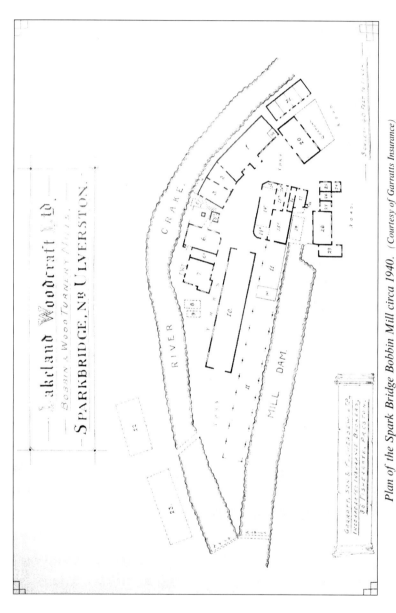

Plan of the Spark Bridge Bobbin Mill circa 1940. (Courtesy of Garratts Insurance)

Garratt, Son and Flowerdew arranged the insurance of the Spark Bridge Bobbin Mill premises for many years. This plan was drawn by Bob Gilleade in the late 1940s when the business was known as Lakeland Woodcraft Ltd. The original key no longer exists. The main mill is marked No. 1; Nos 10, 11, 22 and 23 are the wood sheds

Introduction

When walking in the Lake District one often hears mention of the old bobbin mills that used to exist but which have gone long ago, and in many cases have been forgotten.

Yet once there were more than seventy of these mills in the county we now call Cumbria. They formed a hugely successful industry which year after year produced bobbins in their millions.

Little has been recorded of the daily life of the people who worked in these mills during their heyday and it was this thought that inspired me to write a history about Lakeland bobbin making, and in particular the Philipson family and its connection with the bobbin industry.

For almost 125 years a wood-turning mill was at work in the little village of Spark Bridge, which lies a few miles north of the town of Ulverston. I went to work in the mill in 1929 as a nervous boy of fifteen and at once was caught up in the Victorian atmosphere of the place and the lives of the bobbin makers who worked there. They toiled in their rural environment, often with meagre resources, far removed from our present day and its so-called sophistication and technology. In the pages that follow I have tried to tell a little of their story.

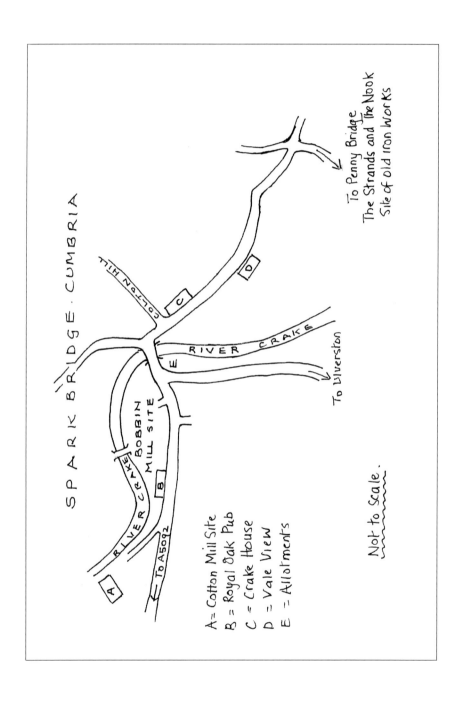

SPARK BRIDGE · CUMBRIA

To Penny Bridge
The Strands and the Nook
Site of old iron works

COLTON HILL

RIVER CRAKE

RIVER CRAKE

BOBBIN MILL SITE

To A5092

To Ulverston

A
B
C
D
E

A = Cotton Mill Site
B = Royal Oak Pub
C = Crake House
D = Vale View
E = Allotments

Not to scale.

Chapter One

New Boy at the Mill

The Cumbrian Bobbin Mill –
Heyday, Decline and Diversification

'Alf, this is my lad,' said my father. 'I want him to learn the business. Put him to work, and there's no favours.' With these words I was introduced to the family business which was almost a century and a quarter old. It was 1929 and I was to be the last of four generations and countless family members who had been connected with the Philipson mills down through the years.

My father and I had walked up the low road to the mill on that particular wet and blowy Monday afternoon, and standing somewhat nervously with my back to the warm radiator in the office I waited.

Alf Westall, the veteran foreman, came in and gave me a curt nod and a 'Come with me'. Equipped with two new swill baskets I was taken to the packing loft to 'help sort out the bobbins'.

In my youthful ignorance I had little or no idea of the background to bobbin making. This had been an industry born from the Industrial Revolution. The invention of railways and steam power had triggered off the biggest boom in industrial history, creating the great mill towns down in Yorkshire and Lancashire. The clothing industry had arrived with a vengeance. Cotton mills sprang up by the score, and their combined appetite for bobbins was colossal.

Lakeland, with its hills and valleys, rivers and becks, was the site of many old industrial mills perfectly suited for conversion to bobbin making; the prime factor being the coppice wood which grew profusely on all sides. As the insatiable demand for cotton increased, so did bobbin making, until more than seventy mills in Lakeland were busily satisfying the ever increasing demand.

The Manchester Cotton Exchange would see the gathering of spinners and bobbin makers. They would discuss the current year's crop of cotton from Alabama and Tennessee. A good yield would mean another year's prosperity. With every garment in the family being made by the women in the house, the market for thread was huge and business prospects encouraging.

Bobbins were counted by the gross. Between 1850 and 1900, at the height of the trade, 350,000 gross was a typical order which might be entrusted to one bobbin mill turner, that is just over five million. Producing approximately 40 bobbins per minute, in a twelve-hour day and six-day week, the turner would require over six months to complete an order of that size. His output was bagged and sent to the cotton spinners, probably at monthly intervals. The demands of the cotton mill kept the bobbin making machines constantly at work. A large cotton mill could handle as many as ten million bobbins per week.

Some bobbin mills were of considerable size, but most were moderate to small operations, located in rural areas and working on small rivers and becks, greatly contrasting with the huge cotton mills of the cotton towns of Lancashire that they supplied. It is likely that big orders would be shared by more than one mill, so as to keep sufficient amounts arriving in time to supply the constant demands of the spinners.

The mammoth orders, however, were not to last. Back in my grandfather's day, the principle cotton spinners got together and formed a Cotton Combine. Their object was to standardisze bobbin sizes, and as a result order quantities increased and went to bobbin mills which were springing up in the Baltic states. The Norwegians in particular possessed great stands of superior Baltic birch, which had almost no knots. Lakeland wood, although perfectly fit for the purpose, had knots and imperfections. Another advantage was the ability to use fully automatic machines which could be run by unskilled labour, producing little or no rejects. From around 1900 the volume of orders began to decline. Lakeland mills got the medium and small orders only, the cream going overseas. Spark Bridge became a mill which predominately produced sewing cotton bobbins, as opposed to mill bobbins. Sewing cotton bobbins were made of one solid piece of wood, holding any amount of thread. Every size and shape was made in hundreds of different patterns. Some were small, about half an inch in diameter and length, and some were up to about eight inches long and five inches in diameter.

An important part of the bobbin trade was the making of moulds and tassels. During the Victorian age of ornate decoration there was a tremendous demand for the most varied shapes and sizes of wooden turned moulds for blinds, mantle cloth fringes, tablecloth fringes, upholstery decoration and heavy velvet curtains. They ranged from tiny beads to big imposing chessmen-type shapes which would be expertly covered with woven silk. Bobbins and moulds didn't stop at being turned; some were 'dished', grooved and recessed, slotted, notched, bored and branded. In addition many bobbins were dyed and polished in yellow and orange, bright red, blue, green and black. There was no end to the various embellishments that were required. We would ask ourselves why the customer would want a particular detail, and seldom ever found out why. The profiles for moulds and tassels required for the trimming trade were just endless. Seasoned turners would be fascinated to see yet another shape appear. Disputes would arise as to whether it had been produced previously. Samples would be gone through, only to prove that the latest tassel was indeed new, and only slightly different from one previously produced. Every different firm in every different trade would require a personalised product, perhaps slightly modified from another pattern.

This was an age of formal communication. A dignified letter of enquiry would arrive, accompanied by a sample bobbin in a little cotton drawstring bag attached to the envelope. Over the years we handled thousands of patterns for different customers and different trades, and they in turn, would vary their requirements. We always kept the samples. They were everywhere. We had drawers full, boxes full, bobbins on strings, bobbins on nails and on every ledge and cupboard. It was impossible for an old firm of this nature to operate without accumulating all kinds of odd quantities put aside for one reason or another. Indeed, it became quite a problem. However, a pleasant surprise often came to light when, for a particular reason, a search was instigated. Shapes and colours would be unearthed, bobbins probably produced decades earlier and long since forgotten. It was rather like going through Granny's old trunk in the attic!

I remember in 1930 finding some old samples on a secluded window ledge in a loft; they were partially demolished into fine powder by woodworms. Some strings hanging on a bobbin slide in the mill had turned a beautiful mellow brown with age and were polished accidentally by being in the line of shavings which came off the machines.

Many products had names which helped to identify them. Some were known as 'Gimp Head', 'Small Strip', 'Register Mould', 'One Ounce', 'Two Ounces', 'Quarter Pound', 'Ten Metre', 'Thirty Metre', 'Convex', and so on. Wire bobbins were known by the diameter of the end flanges, ranging from one inch up to four inches. Many of the latter had a coat of brown shellac varnish applied to the flat edge of the bottom flange. This was done with a brush while the article was rotated slowly on a spindle, the bobbins then being placed on pegged boards to allow them to dry.

Before the turn of the nineteenth century, a large segment of work was the making of pill boxes and ointment boxes from shavings. They were almost like old fashioned hat boxes, only in miniature. I remember seeing samples. They were beautifully made, very neat and accurate. They were made of white heavy shavings, most likely in one or two ounce sizes. I never found anyone who had the slightest knowledge of how they were produced. The whole operation seems to have gone into oblivion with no records kept. Really very sad.

Our home was always fueled with wood from the mill. Usually two scuttles stood near the kitchen stove. One held blocking wood and the other held reject bobbins. Bobbins lit the fire and rejuvenated it.

THREAD BOBBINS

ESTABLISHED A CENTURY

WIRE BOBBINS

WOOD-TURNERY FOR
· - ALL TRADES · ·

THOMAS PHILIPSON

BOBBIN MANUFACTURER

SPARK BRIDGE MILL

GREENODD

ULVERSTON

TOY TRADE

ELECTRICAL

TURNERY BY
MASS PRODUCTION

TRIMMINGS
AND
HANDLE TRADES

Calling card, Thomas Philipson, Bobbin Manufacturer
(Courtesy of the Philipson family)

Outsiders were shocked to see such beautiful shapes and colours committed to the flames. These were the bobbins rejected by the sorters before dispatch. With their bright colours and highly polished surfaces it seemed such a crime to consign them to the fire. My children used to play with them for hours on end, never tiring of the possible wonders they could create with them. It took a practiced eye to find the defects, but the sorting girl in the packing room was rarely wrong. A typical bag of mixed bobbins and tassels would seriously rival any set of children's building blocks on the market today, their variety and shapes and colours were a sure means of firing the imagination.

In 1928 our mill made and delivered one gross of moulds and tassels to a firm in Manchester, carriage paid, for ten pence per gross. An acknowledgement from them stated there would be no further orders. They were able to procure the same article from Japan, carriage paid, plus a twenty per cent tariff for slightly less per gross than the local price.

By 1930 trade was quite reduced at Spark Bridge and to supplement business we went in to what my father called 'variety turning'.

The main segment of production became toy parts. There was no plastic in those days; everything had to be fashioned from wood or metal. We produced parts for many toy companies: toy engines, engine boilers, funnels, whistles and domes, buffers and wheels of all sizes from one inch to six inches. Wheels were a big line, we made a thousand gross. The round circular grain of coppice was particularly suited for the job. The fronts were dished and we painted them in two colours. Handles for dolls' prams, handles for tools: handles for curry combs for the horse trade, fly-swatter handles and reels for fishing lines: knobs of all kinds, household wares, in short – any small object found its way on to the machines. We made millions of rollers for cigarette-making machines, tiny bushes for the electrical trade and motor trade, children's beads for counting frames, finished in ten different colours. We even made moulds to produce rubber balloons. The list seemed never-ending, we never knew what the next enquiry would bring. Many mills ceased to exist during these straightened times. By diversifying, Spark Bridge Mill was able to continue right up to the 1940s in small product lines.

In 1935, the yo-yo craze hit the nation and at the same time our mill at Spark Bridge. The yo-yo was particularly suited for production on our machinery, and the round grained coppice wood made an ideal product. In no time at all we were inundated with orders which meant round-the-clock production. It was impossible to satisfy all demands. Some toy sellers were prepared to drive the length and breadth of the country just to obtain a bag or two. Telegrams arrived in shoals in efforts to get faster results. Sadly, just as quickly as the craze came, so it went. The yo-yo went as dead as a dodo.

The next decade saw the extinction of the wooden sewing cotton bobbin. Did anyone visualise the impact of plastic, coupled with the new synthetic fibres and the revolutionary new processes in the textile industry?

Visiting Spark Bridge in 1978, I was fascinated to see them making big mill bobbins of polished aluminium, and to be told that they sold for twenty pounds each. There was not a shaving or piece of wood to be seen.

Chapter Two

William Philipson

Cunsey to Hugill Mill

My great grandfather, William Philipson (1798–1876), began work in the bobbin trade in the early 1800s at Cunsey Mill, a small picturesque hamlet on the west side of Windermere lake. He must have been a man of some ambition, because we next hear of him as manager for J. Thompson of Goose How Mill at Fellfoot on the River Kent, which lies about a mile north of Staveley. It was an ideal place for a water mill, with the sweeping slopes of the Kentmere Valley to catch the Lakeland rains. He soon became the owner of this mill and by local standards it was considered a reasonably large establishment.

Probably influenced by the booming conditions of the industry, William Philipson decided to build a new and better mill somewhat lower down from the original one. This second mill was regarded as one of the finest in the district and was built specially for the trade, whereas many local bobbin mills were conversions.

We had the original architect's plans of the new Hugill Mill stored away in a belt store at Spark Bridge: it was truly a fine structure. One hundred men were reputed to have worked there, as well as a good number of women and youths. Most of them walked from Kendal every day. With possibly a twelve-hour working day, they would probably only see daylight on Sundays.

I am greatly indebted to Mr John. W. Allen of Fellfoot, for a letter written in November 1847, by William Philipson to a millwright,

John Wilson, giving specifications for a new water wheel, and urging speed as the old one was on its last legs. The technical details in this letter leave no doubt that wheels were designed with the utmost care. These men were highly proficient in wheel manufacture.

William was among the first to install one of the new, recently invented turbines. Apparently, on the first test it failed to perform. The old man must have been beside himself. However it was discovered that a baulk, or timber, wedged in the gears was the only obstruction and the turbine was soon working efficiently.

Regarded as the finest of its kind in the north of England, 178ft long and 45ft wide, Hugill Mill was opened in 1859. William Philipson treated all his workers and their wives to a reception. Tables were laid down the aisles between the machines, which were decorated with evergreens. Chandeliers hung from the roof and the coke stoves warmed the building. The Kendal Brass Band attended. This inauguration was held after the mill had begun production, necessitating the removal of all shavings and dust from the building. It must have been a big job.

A major fire befell the mill in 1866, but it appears to have weathered the storm until about 1895 when the place passed to other hands and four years later closed altogether. The mill stood empty for twenty years and then was systematically dismantled to provide material for cottages. By 1928, not a trace was left, only the wood-sheds gave an indication of any previous existence. I talked with a local man years later who explained with enthusiasm how they toppled the big limestone chimney by knocking out base stones and substituting wood blocks and lighting a fire inside.

Cousins of the Philipson family moved to Keswick around the middle of the nineteenth century and ran mills there successfully for more than a hundred years.

William Philipson had two sons, Thomas and James, who were active in the business and it was left equally to them after his day. Thomas elected to take his half of the machinery and start his own concern.

Chapter Three

Industries of the Crake Valley

When Thomas Philipson came to Spark Bridge in 1850, he entered a valley of vibrant activity. The Crake Valley and the River Crake run from the southern tip of Coniston Lake, down to the sea at Greenodd. A lot had happened on that short and pleasant river before my grandfather arrived there. Many mills dotted the river's edge, but the ones of real interest were at Spark Bridge, Penny Bridge and Newlands, which is on the way to Ulverston.

A fine cotton mill stood on a site just above the dam that serviced what was to become the Spark Bridge Bobbin Mill. This mill, similar to the one at Backbarrow, operated between mid-1700 to the mid-1800s, before falling victim to the centralized industry in South Lancashire. In about1800 a great storm burst the cotton mill dam, sending silt down river to block the mill dam below. The fine limestone building sat idle for many years after the looms and machinery had been hurled from the upstairs windows, and eventually decay and pillaging reducing it to rubble. Two fine undershot wheels, very big and broad, with shallow vanes or buckets, survived until 1927, with a quantity of gearing. Then this fell into the scrap dealers' hands. I remember playing in among those wheels as a boy.

The site which Thomas Philipson acquired for his bobbin mill was the defunct Spark Bridge iron foundry with a history dating back to medieval times. In fact a charter was granted by Elizabeth 1st giving

11

the right to use water from the river 'for ever'. In the early 1700s the place was a bloomery, and later became a forge for the smelting of iron. Various companies appear to have owned and managed it, including the Backbarrow Iron Company who supplied it with pig iron. Numerous iron wares were made, including anchors, chains and sundry items for ships which were being built down-river at Penny Bridge and Greenodd. Iron products appear to have been shipped to many places around the British coast. Eventually, the place was modernized by the Newland Iron Company and worked until 1850.

At Penny Bridge, which is just one and a half miles south of Spark Bridge, there was a similar, well organized iron furnace with an almost identical history of activity in the iron trade. In addition to the many iron wares this place made in the mid-1700s were great quantities of cannon balls. I lived alongside this mill and as a boy roamed the buildings. I remember finding a few rusty cannon balls in a corner, not knowing their significance at the time. Penny Bridge Iron Furnace, like Spark Bridge, was once connected with Newland Iron Furnace and Backbarrow. Penny Bridge appears to have closed down earlier, because it then became a flax mill and ultimately a paper mill for a short period. I believe it closed down around 1870. But as mills go, it remained in a remarkable state of preservation. As boys, we roller skated on the main floor. The power had been two huge breast wheels (long gone), but the wheel pits remained intact well into the twentieth century. There was a fine weir and a long race which gradually dried up and filled in.

My father proved the quality of the pure charcoal iron produced at the Penny Bridge mill. There was a huge stone block lying near the wheel pit. Each corner of the block had embedded in it a one-and-a-quarter inch threaded bolt, and the thread appeared to be still in good condition. We obtained the corresponding nut, and with assistance from a wrench and a drop of oil were able to screw the nut the full length of the thread. Quite a feat considering all the years it had been standing out in the weather.

The walls around the mill were capped with the dross clinkers which were poured into the sand after the smelting. Traces of iron remaining in the clinkers could easily be brightened after a rub with emery cloth, showing no tendency to rust. They really produced pure iron.

The spring tides used to come up the River Crake as far as the old furnace, and for about an hour, when the tide reached its peak, everything went deathly still. Not a leaf moved, not one sound. It was eerie to say the least, especially if it happened around midnight.

A century ago it must have been a 'Dante's Inferno', with the sound of the trip hammers banging from dawn to dusk, producing their iron wares. It made me wonder what major battles were fought with those cannon balls.

Chapter Four

The Philipsons at Spark Bridge

Thomas – Harry – Charles

Thomas Philipson appears to have been a successful and popular man. He obviously knew his trade, having worked with his father at Fellfoot. Converting an old iron furnace into a bobbin mill was no mean feat, but this he did and he appears to have become a man of means in a relatively short time.

Thomas had ten children, the last two being born at Crake House, a house in Spark Bridge which was used as a temporary home before moving into the family home at Vale View. Vale View was a large Georgian style house, with an impressive glass veranda running its full length. It had a short drive, and a semi-circular carriage sweep. The house sat on an elevated ledge, and commanded a magnificent view right down the Crake Valley. A five minute walk down to the mill would appear to be a very convenient arrangement. Extensive gardens and glass houses were maintained and the coach house and barn were just across the road.

My grandfather was quite a walker, and regularly walked right around Coniston Lake on a Sunday afternoon. He was a remarkable shot and a good fly fisherman. Indeed, he was highly regarded by his contemporaries. He once caught three large salmon in one afternoon in the River Leven near Newby Bridge. For years people alluded to the spot as 'Philipson's Pool'. He was a JP and rode into Ulverston most Thursdays to attend to his public duties.

Looking across the River Crake to Vale View at Spark Bridge

When I entered the mill as a boy, old timers repeatedly told me how many years they had worked for him, and how fair he had been as an employer. Sad to say, not all Philipsons were as popular, but I have yet to hear a discordant note about my late grandfather.

Thomas Philipson married Margaret Braithwaite, from the distinguished Crook family who owned a foundry and engineering works. These people invented and produced nearly all the bobbin making machinery for the trade at that time. The marriage of Thomas and Margaret was considered a very good union, at least from a trade point of view.

Thomas Philipson liked his tot of whisky, whilst Margaret, his wife would vehemently denounce drink. A tale was told that one evening, while they were sitting by the fire, Margaret stabbed her needles into her tatting and exclaimed piously, 'Drink should be put down with a firm hand!' Thomas replied, 'I thoroughly agree with you, my dear', and promptly downed his glass behind his newspaper.

For good measure, Thomas would tip whisky into his boots when he went fishing, to 'keep my feet warm', he said.

Later in life, when Thomas was a successful and established business man, he was taken to task by one of his daughters for having frayed cuffs on his jacket. He surveyed the jacket and sagely replied that he could now afford to walk around in shabby clothes!

✠

Harry Philipson was Thomas's oldest son and he assumed the management of Spark Bridge after the death of his father in 1911. However, this arrangement appears to have fallen through and he moved to Greenodd. There he set up a small chemical works, complete with a retort, with the object of extracting 'something' from sawdust and shavings. He became engrossed with his experiments. When his sisters appeared on site with his meals they were horrified to see him jab the cutlery into the sand to clean it. He was quickly dubbed 'Chemical Harry' by the local villagers. Nevertheless, he had a germ of an idea, though he was probably eighty years before his time. Nothing significant appeared to come from his experiments, and the affair died a natural death.

Harry returned to the bobbin mill trade by taking over the bobbin mill at Crooklands. An old employee told me that Harry was a highly excitable person to work for. Apparently he objected to the beck watcher walking through the mill yard on his daily rounds and heated exchanges took place. Apparently both parties had 'rights'. The matter came to a head when they locked horns and both ended submerged in the mill race!

The only time I saw my Uncle Harry, was the day that the old family home, Vale View, was disposed of by Harrisons, the auctioneers of Ulverston. Various brothers and sisters had discreetly gathered for this event. Harry was disembarking from an open touring car, parked in County Square. I remember the brass headlights on the front and a large folded canvas top, looking like a giant horse collar draped round the back of the body. He was a tall angular man, with snowy

Thomas Philipson 1837–1911
(*Courtesy Philipson family*)

Margaret Philipson (nee Braithwaite)
1842–1928 (*Courtesy Philipson family*)

The Philipson family photographed at Vale View, Spark Bridge, probably not long before Thomas Philipson's death in 1911. Thomas and Margaret are seated at the front. Their son John Braithwaite is standing far left and Thomas Charles stands third from the right. Other members of the family include William Henry, Philip, Robert Crake, Charlotte, Dora May, Maud, Ethel Mary and Jessie.
(*Courtesy Philipson family*)

17

Charles Philipson (1875–1955) and Ida Philipson (dates not known)
(Courtesy of the Philipson family)

Charles and Ida with their young family. Left to right: Douglas, Dorothy,
Kathleen, Charles. (Courtesy of the Philipson family)

18

white hair and a battered old trilby hat with the broad rim turned down all round. He wore a stiff khaki canvas raincoat, very long and unbuttoned, held from flapping open by a belt. An aunt pointed him out to me, saying, 'That's your Uncle Harry, the old so-and-so!' thereby perpetuating the petty differences for which the Philipsons had been famous for so many years.

After my grandfather's death, the proceeds of the mill went to my grandmother, and the place was to be managed by two of her sons under the guidance of Charles (my father), Maud (a daughter) and Dr Bowman from Ulverston (a trustee). My grandmother appears to have been something of a martinet, and would not allow one penny to be spent on improvements or repairs. Consequently, we had on our hands a very old business, struggling grievously for want of a face lift. After grandmother's death in 1928, both the house and mill were to be sold. However one son and one daughter put their resources together and kept the old business within the family. My father, Charles, was to be manager.

Father left college to be an apprentice ironmonger. He proved to have a strong mechanical bent all his life and became a fine model engineer. His first job was with John Albright, who had a shop in New Market Street in Ulverston. They had three or four apprentices in those days. The shop next door was Birkett's, the drapers. It is possible that Norman Birkett was serving his time as a draper at this juncture. Father recounted tales of many high jinks in Albright's cellars. John Albright sold wire rat traps and stove pipes and elbows. He also kept ferrets in his basement. It didn't take long for the apprentices to think up an amusing game. The lads placed a line of stove pipe around the four walls of the cellar, using elbows at the corners, but allowing a gap of about an inch at each junction. Next day they caught a rat in one of the traps. To liven up the tempo of an otherwise dull day, they placed the rat in the stovepipe race-way, followed by the ferret. The ensuing performance was highly satisfactory, until old man Albright was heard coming downstairs. Needless to say, total confusion reigned, three or four apprentices frantically trying to catch the rat and the ferret, and dispose of them as quickly as they could without being discovered.

Father travelled to different jobs in Yorkshire, and eventually set up his own business in Wednesbury, Staffordshire. In the 1920s the belching chimneys and dirty industries there gave credence to its nickname, the Black Country. A truly depressing area.

We were a family of six children living in a terrace house, with father spending all his waking hours at his shop. His main interest was his workshop which was upstairs, where he did all-and-sundry jobs for many people. Not for him the mundane task of selling merchandise over the counter, his staff attended to that. Those were the days of repair and fix, and he had a good reputation for getting any gadget or piece of machinery back into working order.

During this period, father was a trustee for his mother's mill in the Lake District and, being a competent engineer, he received many frantic calls whenever they were in trouble. One of the first calls came in 1924 as the result of a fire. The old boiler-house and kiln went up in flames early one morning. Although workers and villagers turned out in the pre-dawn, very little could be saved. The mill, without the means of drying its blocks, was in an impossible situation. During his trips north, my father built a new kiln and boiler-house. He also repaired the weir and fitted new clews and replaced the old wooden pentrough with a steel one. He also built a new private bridge to span both sides of the timber yard.

When the old bridge was demolished, it became clear that the vertical timbers supporting it had been standing on smooth rock in the centre of the river with no anchorage at all. When this was discovered, Jim Pattinson the carter was aghast. Had he known, he said, he would never have taken his horses over such a flimsy structure. The fact that his own safety might be in jeopardy never crossed his mind.

The new kiln and boiler house was built of brick and metal with an asbestos roof, nothing whatever inflammable. The new Lancashire

Douglas Philipson and family *(courtesy of the Philipson family)*

The Strands, Penny Bridge. This was Douglas's childhood home. He moved to The Nook, an adjoining property, after his marriage to Catherine.

(courtesy of the Philipson family)

21

boiler was eighteen feet in diameter and sixty feet long, with two three-foot fire tubes. A man by the name of David Greenhow loaded it onto his steam traction engine at Greenodd with the use of L.M.S. cranes. After the journey, which consisted of some tortuous bends, he off-loaded it as near as possible to its ultimate resting place. For this entire service, he charged only five pounds.

In 1926, we moved as a family from the Midlands to Penny Bridge, just a short distance from the bobbin mill at Spark Bridge.

Chapter Five

Iron Furnace to Bobbin Mill

*The Design and Construction
of the Spark Bridge Bobbin Mill*

The mill site as old Thomas would find it in the late 1850s was triangular, with the apex to the north and most of the buildings of the iron furnace situated on the left, adjoining the race. The main structure was always alluded to as 'the old Mill'. It had a complex beam and roof system and its continued existence defied logic, it was so old. An old water wheel sufficed to run this structure, probably a leftover from the forge days. Thomas appears to have used this source of power as long as he remained in the old building. In 1870, when the new mill was built it became a coppice barn.

The new mill was built on a site at the extreme right of the property adjoining the river edge. This necessitated abandoning the old water wheel and installing two fine Gilkes vortex steam turbines so that the power could be diverted in a more easterly direction to the new structure.

The new mill was well built and certainly fit for the job in hand at the time. The exterior was of cut Lakeland stone, single storey, topped with an imposing high cathedral-type roof, finished with slate and skylights. The mill bell sat on the ridge at the village end of the structure. The interior was equally well finished, the walls being skimmed in white plaster. The many large windows were set back with thirty inch window sills, a fan light in the top of each one. The floor was paved with large blue flagstones, probably brought from

Order 540 Thos. Philipson March 23/85

16 N/p on 12 ft. } N. Sons.
Rw 120 } 33" Wheel Vertical
30' supply 20' suction.
4" Standard. 3 7/8 Max on.

Case One base shell cast in one piece
Two loose centres.
Two Wheel covers bord 4 1/2
Two 20" Bends.

Wheel One 33" Wheel Wrt Iron

Guide B Four Wrt Iron Guide Blades
Wrt Iron pieces
Gear. 2 Bellcranks 6 1/2 c b c 1 bord 3 1/2
2 Cranks 6 1/2 c b c " 2 1/4
one 2" Worm Wheel " 2 1/2
One 2" Worm Single " 1 3/4
One Bracket & side piece bord 3 1/2 + 1 3/4
One Hand Wheel " 1 3/4

Shaft 1 f 4 1/2

Order for new turbines for the Spark Bridge Mill, 1885

(Courtesy of the Philipson family)

24

Kirkby Quarry. The combination of plenty of glass and a high roof produced a light airy place in which to work. Down the floor in the centre stood a row of cast iron stanchions, capped with iron shoes to hold the big Columbian pine beams and trusses to support the massive roof.

The interior furnishings consisted of double beam benches covering the south half of the floor, one set against each side wall and two sets down the centre, a few feet apart from each other. The building was designed to accommodate the turning lathes by simply placing them on top of the double beams and bolting them from underneath. One quarter of the floor held boring, 'rincing' and roughing machines, which stood on their foundations. The final quarter held saws of all sizes and blocking machines. Various wooden bunks were fitted where possible to accommodate half produced stock. We now have the old mill and the new mill. The workers regularly alluded to them as such.

Thomas Philipson, like his father before him, gave an inaugural feast inside the new mill, very similar to the one held at Fellfoot. Older workers talked of the event with nostalgia as many as fifty years later. The mill had apparently sported a drum and fife band in bygone days. This gem of knowledge was passed on to me as a child by an aunt who told me that the last surviving drum was still in the warehouse down at the post office. Hot foot, and arriving breathless, I begged Mrs Westall to let me search for it. Our search was fruitless which was perhaps a blessing.

The River Crake ran down to the right of the complex of buildings, the race down the left and the underground tailrace across the bottom, back to the river. The race left the dam narrow and defined, but widened like a leg of mutton before reaching the clews and pentrough which received the water over the turbines. The new pentrough was a steel structure supported by iron girders. Every annual holiday it was scraped and re-done with red lead paint. Not one speck of rust was allowed to develop.

The turbines below were a remarkable design and thanks were due to their makers, Gilkes of Kendal. The water was forced through the

The new mill interior showing the belts running from the main shafts. 'From the ground level there appeared to be belts going everywhere and they waved and flapped in an alarming way' (Courtesy Eileen Thompson)

A view of the mill looking towards the office. The saws and blocking machines are seen on the right. Note the lengths of coppice on the floor and stools made from tree trunks (Courtesy Eileen Thompson)

A view of the mill showing the boring, rincing and roughing machines. These interior photographs were taken at Spark Bridge circa 1935. (Courtesy Eileen Thompson)

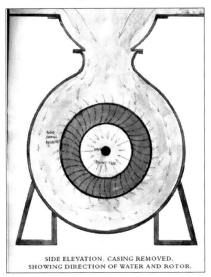

SIDE ELEVATION. CASING REMOVED.
SHOWING DIRECTION OF WATER AND ROTOR.

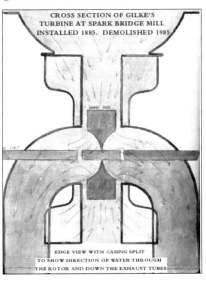

CROSS SECTION OF GILKE'S
TURBINE AT SPARK BRIDGE MILL
INSTALLED 1885. DEMOLISHED 1985

EDGE VIEW WITH CASING SPLIT
TO SHOW DIRECTION OF WATER THROUGH
THE ROTOR AND DOWN THE EXHAUST TUBBS

Water turbines at Spark Bridge. This diagram by Douglas Philipson depicts the water turbines supplied by Gilkes of Staveley. Gilkes is still manufacturing turbines today. (Courtesy of the Philipson family)

perimeter of the wheels and out of the centre, and then vacuumed down through exhaust tubes into the pit below. This principle used every drop of water to give maximum power. In about 1935, it was decided that it was time the turbines should be opened and inspected. They had run for about sixty-five years. Great energy was expended to try to open the huge casing, resulting in a gap of about nine inches, still not big enough to see inside. The smallest boy in the place, Jimmie McGee, who came from Quebec Street in Ulverston, was the man of the hour. Small and thin, he was able to crawl inside and report. After all those years, the bronze buckets were in perfect condition and still showed their machinery marks. Jimmie was very proud of himself that day and went home with an extra ten bob!

Under the turbines was a rock pool running out into the tail-race, its path going under the smithy, the entrance yard, the new mill and into the river. The water way was stone built with an arched roof. Following the same route, above the tunnel went the power shaft, with inspection lids for bearings at intervals. One of these trap doors was in the office floor in the corner of the mill, the shaft rumbling away under the office desk. Just through the door, into the mill proper, emerged a pair of bevel gears, a vertical shaft up to the beams, and a second set of gears. This arrangement brought the power to the main shaft, running the full length down the centre of the beams overhead.

Thirty inch diameter spoke wheels with flat polished edges from four to eight inches broad, were fitted to the shaft at close intervals for its full length. These drums, as they were called, carried the belts to the four lines of machines below. From the ground level there appeared to be belts going everywhere and they waved and flapped in an alarming way, often knocking a man's hat off. The belts carried power to any piece of equipment on the floor, no matter where it was placed, and yet it came from one source, the overhead shaft.

The bevel gears connecting the power and main shafts had a steel pinion which drove a heavy four-foot iron crown wheel with wooden teeth for silent running. Eventually these teeth would become dangerously thin through constant wear, and would have to be replaced. The process was a good example of the old millwright's art.

New teeth were procured in blank form and lived on the kiln for more than a year. The wood was hornbeam. After the old teeth had been removed, with much difficulty, the new ones had their shanks wrapped in sailcloth and daubed with red lead. They were driven in with a heavy mallet until all had bottomed. Locking rods were secured on the back side. Now came the important process of paring. The teeth required a profile somewhat like a spoon to accommodate the steel pinion, and 24-inch-long chisels in razor-sharp condition were used and the greatest care taken to profile the hardwood teeth perfectly. Once the paring had reached a certain stage, a smear of black grease was put on the steel pinion and the whole power structure was carefully hauled round by hand. Any imperfect teeth were marked and pared a little more. This trial and error method lasted until every tooth engaged and withdrew from the pinion perfectly. To run a mill with the crude and simple principle of wooden teeth required clever men.

From river to machinery … what a wonderful means of free power was at our disposal. All it cost was a drop of oil in the turbines' bearings once a week, and the physical effort required to lift the sluice gates to allow the water to flow. It was possible to run the whole complex for any reason, day or night. Often Alf, our foreman, would require power to perfect a turning lathe. He would merely wind down the clew gate as he went into the door of his home, which was alongside the turbines.

Our situation was enviable; picturesque surroundings with free power, and our raw materials grown almost on the doorstep, local village labour, and taxes so low they were hardly noticeable. Add to this free boiler heat and steam from wood waste. Not many concerns could boast of such advantages.

Chapter Six

Leaves and Eels
and Other Interruptions

Water power was wonderfully tranquil: the silent flow of water down the race and constant gentle hum of the turbines. No complicated engines or dynamos to break down or burn out. However, there were variations in the strict tempo. Leaves found their way into the system and were a problem in the autumn. They would float down by the thousand. Vertical bars were placed in the race just before the clew gates, and this area would matt with leaves so densely as to seriously slow down the entire unit. During the worst period, a boy was periodically detailed to rake these grids.

Eels also found their way into the system but my father turned this to his advantage. He diverted a water pipe from the race into an old tank with a perforated lid on top. The water cascaded into this for days and leaked out of the smaller holes. Then came the day of inspection. Lo and behold, the tank was a mass of writhing eels! To combat their sliminess a swillfull of sawdust was thrown among them and they were packed into plywood tea boxes and sent to Manchester Fish Market. The river was better for being rid of its worst predator.

Heavy floods could be a problem too, but Spark Bridge hardly ever suffered in this respect. An abnormally high river would back up the tail race and impede the water flow trying to get down. Although some mills came to a standstill with this problem, Spark Bridge was rarely affected.

The classic interruption was shortage of water created by a dry spell. As the river's level dropped daily the mill managed to keep going, but by mid-afternoon the speed would lag. Within a day or two it would be necessary to stop for a short while to fill the dam race. Without rain the situation would worsen and the decision would be taken to operate a night shift. This would mean halving the power requirements and conserving water.

Night shift for young people was quite attractive. Cool summer nights with very little authority and a change in routine were all very pleasant. Nevertheless, even with a night shift the mill would come to a standstill for lack of water. A prime opportunity for mischief! Between the two woodsheds a cloud of bats would fly backwards and forwards. We stood at each end and bombarded them with blocks.

With the water still, a smooth rock pool lay under the wheels of the turbine and a check might reveal one or two fine salmon resting. This would be the signal for action. At two or three in the morning the smithy fire would be hastily lit and iron heated and pounded on the anvil in an all-out effort to manufacture a gaff hook or leister. Alas, the water was 'up', the mill started and it was a case of back to work.

Chapter Seven

A Coppice Mill

Supply – Delivery – Peeling – Sizing
– Stacking – Coppice Men

A walk up the yard with its two huge drying sheds proved Spark Bridge to be truly a coppice mill. The shed beyond the old mill, alongside the race, must have been the biggest drying shed in the district. I don't have the dimensions of its enormous height and length but it still stands. Strangely, some of the stone pillars are taper-round and some square. The taper-round character suggests an earlier structure than 1850 when the place was converted from iron to bobbins. Probably it was a huge charcoal barn, later adapted to coppice. The lower bays were altered latterly to accept machinery with lofts above. The two top bays were taken down before the Second World War to give more yard space.

The second shed stood in the centre of the main yard, wider than the first, with a high slated roof, standing on traditional Lakeland stone columns on both sides. After the war this shed was completely enclosed and became a well organized heavy sawmill.

Across the bridge stood two more mammoth sheds of a different design. One-foot square pitch pine posts supported a corrugated iron roof. Both had a great capacity and coppice poles were piled up to the roof every year, holding many many tons. Coppice wood, by nature, is light compared to heavy timber logs and although men stacked it as well as possible, the bends and elbows prohibited solid stacking. Nevertheless we carried 5,000 tons when all stacks were full.

These two huge wood sheds were situated across the river from the mill yard at Spark Bridge. (Courtesy of the Philipson family)

The iron and wood sheds stood for well over a century, the corrugated iron being many times thicker than any made today. One or two of the posts were dug out before the war and lifted a little. They proved to be sitting in silver sand and no rot was evident after all those years.

Coppice poles came from every direction. The wood grew in every valley and was owned mainly by farmers and large estates. A woodcutter would negotiate to acquire the cutting rights and come to the mill with a glowing account of how he now owned a marvellous stand of birch or ash, and pleading with my father to 'just come and have a look'. A price was fixed and the main crop being bobbin wood came into the mill. Only birch, ash, sycamore, alder, hazel and rowan were suitable for bobbins.

The coppice poles were cut and trimmed and loaded onto farmers' two-wheel carts, with the thin end of the poles over the horses' back. A little book was kept in the weigh-house, and every load was weighed in and noted. In the 1930s wood came in over the scale

A view of the two wood sheds in the mill yard taken at Spark Bridge. Two men can be seen stacking. Note the round and square pillars of the large coppice barn.

Sized coppice wood. Note the method of stacking.

34

costing sixteen to eighteen shillings per ton, sometimes having been trekked for miles in appalling weather. Often it would arrive after dark in pouring rain, and the woodman would have to unload in the yard in total blackness, or at best, by the aid of a shippon lamp.

Heavy timber came in on pole wagons, usually pulled by three horses. It was quite a job after dark to steady the front wheels on the scale and then the rear wheels, while the horses were jumping at the sounds of the circular saws. These heavy trees were chained with a clamp device. The driver would release the clamp and instantly the load burst off the wagon. It was a dangerous procedure and the man had to be extremely agile to jump clear. I have seen some very close shaves in our yard.

Once summer was over and the leaves were falling from the trees, the sap ceased to rise and the woodcutters got going. The autumn and early winter was a busy time in the yard of a bobbin mill. Soon piles of coppice poles were lying everywhere. The constant problem was to get them out of the way as there seemed to be a daily stream of carts bringing still more.

The first process was peeling, a method of opening the bark at intervals to speed the drying. A 'peeling horse' was used, which consisted of a sturdy pole set on four legs stuck in at angles, allowing the pole to be about bench height. Two short forks of coppice wood similar to a tuning fork, one in each end sticking upright, completed the horse. This portable contraption was placed alongside a chosen stack of wood. The peeler would lift a coppice pole onto the two forks, and begin cutting long gashes into the back on the near and off-side, alternately with a two-handed drawknife. Once at the end of the pole, he turned the wood over and worked to the original end again. The resulting four lines of cuts roughly spaced around the wood were a considerable help when seasoning. Despite this, all wood took its time to season, usually about two years, though ash, which didn't respond to peeling, required four or five years before it was reliable to use.

Peeling was a changeable occupation from the worker's point of view. When the wood was freshly cut, small in diameter and straight and clean, one felt at peace with the world. To hear the birds singing, one felt wonderful to be away from the confines of the mill. On the other hand, the wood could be large in diameter, long cut with craggy bark which defied the knife. It would probably be a cold wet day, the poles slimy with mud and the worker with an old sack round his waist and another round his shoulders. His feet would be like ice, standing on muddy ground all day long. Working in an isolated place, the job was classed as piece work, the pay being two and a half pence per score. A lot of peeling was done by casual labour from the local village. They could start and stop as they saw fit, provided they kept the yard foreman informed.

I remember one old man, well over seventy, who lived in a tiny cottage, presumably with no other income than the ten shillings a week old age pension. He wasn't a native, and in his day had travelled around the Horn 'before the mast' in early sailing ships. He would wander up the yard around 9.30 am and at about ten o'clock would go home for a rum and coffee, returning about eleven. At the end of the week we had to break the news to him that he had only earned four shillings and sixpence. 'Don't worry a thing about it,' he would say. 'Money isn't everything. My house is stacked full of treasury notes. You can hardly get through the door for wads of bills on chairs and tables. I wish the wife would get rid of it all!'

Similar conditions prevailed among the stackers. Their job was to load the peeled poles onto big clumsy carts with wooden shafts (which seemed to have been built for a horse but were always man-handled) and trundle them to the appropriate bay for stacking. Again, pleasant in nice weather, but many a day the men were soaked in the driving Lakeland rain, despite being rigged out in sacks from head to toe. There were few complaints and it was with a note of pride that a man would point to a giant shed of probably a thousand tons of timber, and say 'I stacked that last year'. Not for him a cosy job down in the mill.

Tree trunks with a diameter up to thirty inches were labelled 'heavy timber'. This wood was usually unloaded as near the big saw as possible. The men would cut it into lengths of approximately five feet, with double-handle saws. (No chain saws in those days). Sometimes it was necessary to split the logs with steel wedges. Four men would manhandle a log onto the saw bench, using a pole across the front and one across the back. They would then rip it into halves and quarters. This was green timber and known as blocking wood.

One of the perks of working in the yard was being away from the scrutiny of the foreman, and the chance to keep an eye on the river when the fish were coming upstream. A good salmon or trout had better be wary on those days!

One chap in the yard was Eddie Dickinson, the 'sizing' man. He lived with his old mother in a tiny cottage about a mile down the road at the little hamlet called Little Dicks. Eddie never left the area and was the last of a large family who had gone their separate ways. He was particularly proud of his eldest brother who began as a footman for the Cavendish family at Holker Hall and finally became butler to the famous Venderbilt family in their Fifth Avenue mansion in New York. Eddie was born with a deformity in his hips which made walking very difficult and his daily work was somewhat remarkable. His job was to take one of the lumber bogeys with long shafts up the yard and load it with coppice to bring down to the sizing saw. This entailed climbing on top of big stacks of wood and throwing his requirements down. With a load of almost a ton, he made the return trip to the outside corner of the mill where the saw was located. The journey was all downhill with his hands on the shafts, and the ends of the poles sticking into his neck and shoulders. He came at an ever increasing speed with little control, before making a dramatic u-turn just before he reached the saw. Woe betide anyone that got in his way!

The poles were cut roughly to four foot lengths and thrown into piles of ten different sizes. 'Tops' were number ten and were barely one and a half inches in diameter. The number ones were roughly about five inches in diameter. As the men worked, sticks were hurled in all directions. To the layman, it meant total confusion, but they never made a mistake. When the area became congested, each size was wheeled away on wheelbarrows to be stacked.

The method of stacking sized lumber was unique. A neat assembly, four feet thick and about fifteen feet high, would be thrown up wherever there was a place. Forks of coppice wood were placed on the ground, two pointing inwards from each end. Four uprights were set in the crutch of the forks and acted as end-stops for the stack. More forks were added half way up and again near the top. The weight of the load held the stack together. It was easily erected and just as easily dismantled.

Lakeland dialect was rife. Many words and expressions peculiar to the trade would tax a total stranger. Birch was known as 'birk', sycamore was the 'plain tree', which described its grainless appearance. Alder was pronounced 'Ella'. Ash was alluded to as 'Esh', although Alf always told us to 'do the h'ash first'. On no account should there be any 'yak' (oak). Oak was unsuitable for bobbins.

A recurring irritation was the condition of the wood. If it had grown on swampy ground, or had been felled and left lying in the wood, varying conditions showed up in the machining. The wood would show signs of rot, or would be hard and tough, blunting the tools. Tempers would fray; extra rejects narrowed a man's profit margins. Porous wood was referred to contemptuously as 'fluff balls'.

Woodmongers were a pretty solid segment of society in those days. They faithfully came around prior to cutting time to sell their wares, just like any other salesman. There was a great difference however; no Saville Row suit or smart company car. These men would have the heaviest of boots, corduroy breeches, and leather leggings and a worn tweed jacket. A horse and cart would be their transport. Anything but refined, they were a sturdy, honest breed of men, their word being their bond.

To name a few: there was Tom Nicholson from Bouth, who always arrived with his son, bringing two cartloads of wood together; Mashiter of Newby Bridge; Allenby of Oxenpark; Arthur Kellet of Bandrake Head; and James Croasdale of Haverthwaite. Sometimes farmers would come to offer a few acres of bobbin wood on their land, just ripe for cutting. Once the crop had been viewed and a price agreed, the woodcutter would disappear into his wood, to be lost for weeks or months, while he pursued his lonely craft.

Chapter Eight

Alf Westall

Alf Westall was an institution at Spark Bridge Mill. He worked there for more than fifty years. His grandfather before him had worked for more than fifty years for William Philipson at the mill at Fellfoot, near Staveley. There was a tale passed down relating to the old man. Apparently he began work as a youth, starting at the mill in the middle of the week. A fellow worker asked how he liked the bobbin mill. He replied 'I'll stick it 'til Friday'. That he stayed for fifty years is truly remarkable, and together the two men set an unprecedented record.

Alf was well built, broad shouldered with a fresh healthy complexion. He was quite bald and had a strong nose which carried steel rimmed glasses. He wore a heavy brimmed cap – the peak seeming to curve over his face – and a grey denim suit with the collarless jacket buttoned up to the neck. His boots were quite large and he had an awkward gait. His appearance was of a prosperous farmer, but his quiet voice and few words would dispel this myth.

Alf's loyalty to the company and his job was beyond the bounds of normal employment, even for those days, and he was an indispensable employee. Over a period of forty years, under the management of my two grandparents, three uncles and a hired manager, Alf steadily kept the business running smoothly. His faithful and consistent attention to every detail indicated that in the true sense of the word he was the manager. His only outside interest was the tiny Wesleyan Chapel, which stood on the hill above the village. It had a meagre following in those days, opening for afternoon service every other Sunday. Alf would walk up and light the stove in advance and generally act as verger. Indeed, he had a clerical manner about him, a man of few words, soft spoken and tending to speak in a profound way. He would have made a good minister.

Alf's relationship with the workforce however wasn't always harmonious. Rough, truculent village lads sorely tried him and to their abuse he would say quietly 'Don't be h'impudent!' He was known to send a youth home for three days, 'out to grass'. The disgrace and lack of pay was a powerful deterrent. Everyone with a distasteful job put the blame on Alf, particularly the lads. Looking for a change in our routine always met with the same response. Alf would be working on 'his' machine as we approached with two empty swills to indicate that we had now finished. Alf's reply was a long drawn-out 'Oh' and he would lean on the long handle of his turning machine and vacantly stare into space. This seemed to last a lifetime. Our fate hung in the balance. It was sheer torture. Finally he would say 'Well go and do so and so'. Heavens! This would be even worse than the previous job and we would slink away in despair.

Without doubt he was the senior craftsman. All new and complex jobs he handled on his own turning lathe. He could forge big profile tools, working in the smithy for hours shaping the metal. One of the lads would act as striker with the sledge hammer. No matter how difficult, no product got the better of him. He would perfect it and then hand the turning of the order over to an operator. I remember one particular job he had worked on for days, finally finishing it on a Saturday afternoon. I complimented him on his success. He replied in a somewhat reverent tone 'My boy you may as well make your work a pleasure, rather than a misery, because you have got to do it.' His words had a profound effect on me ever afterwards.

Alf's daily duties began in the early hours. Leaving the rear of the village shop, where he lived, and carrying his lamp (which he took everywhere) he opened the dark mill with huge keys. He'd grease the gears and pull the long chain which activated the bell. People came out of the blackness, lamps would be lit and the day would start. Every man's job, every process, every batch was under his control. The vintage of every stack of timber was locked in his mind, he knew where everything was. He saw to everything. He stepped into the office only when picking up a new order; from then on he was in charge until the LMS railway accepted responsibility for the mill's output. Many wagons and carts came over the scale; people were always looking for Alf to come and 'weigh' them. He accepted the dues for every bag of shavings and every bag of firewood. He issued all the supplies from the stores, his duties were endless.

Long after everyone had gone Alf would lock up and make his way home by the light of his lamp.

Chapter Nine

From Block to Bobbin

*Blocking – Boring – Rincing – Roughing –
Drying – Damping – Turning*

Under Alf's direction, a sawyer would take the appropriate size poles from the stack and set his saw to a specified length. The blade was approximately two feet in diameter and amply powerful, allowing the man to cut his wood into round blocks at the rate of one per second. 'Elbows' had to be eliminated by cutting out small wedges. The saw had almost no table, allowing the man to adjust the wood to maintain right-angle cuts.

Ted Bell was a proficient sawyer. He also had a hot temper and a passion for poaching. Some lad would tip off Ted that there was a salmon in the pool and in moments he would have disappeared. Minutes later Alf would miss the 'chirp, chirp' of Ted's saw. On re-appearing Ted would receive a verbal blistering for leaving his job, whereupon he would lose his temper and put on the greatest show of super fast sawing one could ever see. As lads, we were fascinated and stood at a respectful distance to watch. Alas, Ted passed on very early in life.

Once sawn to size the short blocks were ready to be taken to the work benches for hand boring, their irregular diameters not being suitable for automatic boring machines. The blocks would usually range from three to eight inches in length.

From now, on each stage in the manufacturing process was done 'on the hole'. The hole was the foundation of every bobbin that was ever made. Roughly speaking, the bobbin revolved on some form of spindle while being roughed, rinced, turned, grooved and finished. Most holes were approximately the diameter of the common wooden pencil, but could range upwards to one inch diameter. A belt-driven spindle with a pointed bit, ten inches long, was used for hand boring. The bit was a half diameter rod, hollowed out inside and pointed with what was known as a 'spoon bit'. Fashioning, sharpening and tempering of these bits was very similar to the process of turning tools. Nevertheless, the bit had its own peculiarities and needed an expert to make it perform efficiently.

The task of the hand borer was to get the hole in the middle all the way through, so that the blocks would rough out clean all the way round. Irregular hand boring could make a lot of blocks useless by leaving ugly marks on the bobbins. The block was grasped in both hands, almost like taking hold of a golf shaft. The worker sat on a bench facing the bit, which was revolving at three thousand revs per minute. If all went well and the operator didn't lose his nerve, with two or three moderate pushes and the same number of seconds, a neat parallel hole was bored approximately in the centre. This process needed skill and an inner sense of feel. If the operator 'let go' he received an awful shock which resulted in a mad scramble to grip the spindle and get the bit out. The bit would bend at the neck, the block would fly, often catching the chap in the face or leg or cutting his hands. A bawling out from the foreman for being asleep completed the experience. Great skill was needed to 'true' the bit again.

In bygone days, no man or boy was allowed to choose his job, but the art of hand boring was a skill you instinctively had or had not. The best exponent of the art was a lad called Bob Longmire, who was a bad walker. His legs, ankles and feet all seemed to go in different directions. We came to the conclusion that this was the formula for boring true holes in irregular blocks!

The roughing process was the means of taking off the bark and reducing the block to a diameter slightly more than the finished product. A bobbin with big ends and narrow barrel (a wire bobbin) would probably have its centre portion removed during this process to ease the strain at the turning stage.

Various types of machine were used for roughing, but they were based on the turning machine principle, i.e. headstock, tailstock and tool slide. I can remember one dramatic method: the block was placed on the tailstock pin, immediately it was pulled to the headstock with the right hand and the blade introduced from the back by means of a strap around the operator's waist. He merely jerked his back to do the job, possibly forty times a minute all day long. The price was three farthings per gross (plus a ten-hour day). We didn't know so much about the human spine as we know now. A lot of machines were pedal operated and we worked them at furious speeds on piecework. It called for split-second timing by hands, feet and head.

The bobbin's hole was cleaned of any whiskers by a process known as rincing. The monotony of rincing five hundred gross of bobbins, which cut and burnt our hands, made it an unpopular task.

The short blocks were thrown onto a perforated sliding table to remove all sawdust, and then weighed in swills on a scale before being humped down to the kilns to dry out the sap.

The four kilns at Spark Bridge were situated next to the barrel house and packing loft, two above, two below. These kilns were kept at varying temperatures by steam pipes from the boiler-house and main kiln. A lot of laborious effort went into carting hundreds of gross of blocks or bobbins in swills to be spread on the slatted floors. No automatic conveyers in those days. Kiln work was cosy in winter but unbearable in summer. On rainy days men put their sodden outer clothing in a kiln after riding on their bicycles to work. It was one of the few perks of the job. Rats frequented the warm areas and the men were not allowed to eat food near the kiln so as not to encourage them.

Hundreds of blocks fresh from the kilns were removed to huge storage bunks which stood on stilts over the river. This allowed moisture to re-enter the wood and mellow it. Snuff dry wood, straight off the kiln would not respond to smooth turning. The blocks were tipped into the bunks from an overhead walkway. Below was a small trap door allowing the bobbins to empty through a narrow 'ginnel' into a swill. Backwards and forwards came the operator for more blocks to bore on his machine.

Sometimes a rat would set off an avalanche of blocks in the bunk, and it would be crushed to death. Out would come a lad for a swill load and find an opportunity too good to miss. The corpse, carefully hidden amongst the bored blocks would be delivered into the turner's hopper. Constantly pulling his machine handle with his right hand, he had a habit of raking his blocks out to the front of his hopper with his left hand without looking. Waiting for his reaction was well worth it!

The prepared blocks were now ready for the turning process to transform a rough piece of wood into a bobbin. Swill loads of blocks were hauled up from the storage bunks to keep the turners going. Each lathe had a tapered wooden hopper above it, the load going in over the top. Delivered on the shoulder was the most practical way but the dust covered floor made it hazardous underfoot and a boy needed to crouch to avoid the flying belts as he went backwards and forwards.

The turning lathes were not complicated as such, and fell into two types. The half self-actor (the term semi-automatic hadn't yet arrived) consisted of the headstock, which carried the spindle and flywheel, a front and back saddle which carried all the cutting tools, and the tailstock, which opened and closed the machine and controlled the complete operation by pulling on one handle and pushing it back. The machine did all the small reels and was capable of fabulous quantities. Forty bobbins per minute, or more.

The hand slide was simpler. The front and back saddles or tool blocks were operated by a separate lever and similarly, the tailstock was opened and closed by a simple push-pull lever. Nevertheless, this machine was capable of producing a never ending variety of work; it was the work horse of the trade. Anything of a difficult nature went onto this machine, from the smallest to the largest, and from the most delicate to the most robust.

The bobbin block was placed on the stationery tail pin and pulled onto the revolving mandrel by the action of the tailstock lever. The mandrel had 'wings' or 'feathers' protruding from the first inch. There may have been three, five or seven depending on the size and diameter of the product. This was the gripping device to keep the block revolving while the shaping took place. The overhead handle was now gently pushed in, engaging all the front tools. Now the handle was withdrawn, engaging tools on an overhead frame known as the heading frame. These were shaping and trimming tools. Continuing the stroke towards him the operator finally brought in the end tools which trimmed the ends neatly down to the spindle. The machine was finally pushed to the half-way position, to allow the tailstock to retract. A revolving ring suspended around the mandrel was the method used to draw the bobbin off and shoot it down under the machine into a swill.

There was a fully automatic bobbin turning machine, always alluded to as the self-actor. It carried out all the above functions, the blocks simply being fed down a hopper by a youth. The faults in British timber however tended to make this machine unsuitable.

Occasionally a mistake would involve the batch being reworked. One sage character would mutter 'There's never time to do it right first time, but all the time in the world to do it over again'. Huge quantities, simple processes, and youths, were the ingredients for a restless situation. One day, a youth tapped on the office door and asked timidly if he could have a change of job. When asked what was wrong with the job he had, he replied 'It's boring'. Pressed as to which job that might be, he said 'I'm on the boring machine'!

Hard wood was helped onto the turning spindle with the introduction of a smear of household lard into the hole. Lard was favoured because it did not stain the wood.

The turner's spindle in the headstock was quite substantial, having a diameter of about three inches and running in heavy brass bearings. These spindles had to remain absolutely free of the slightest vibration or the end of the bobbins would develop a 'phonograph record' appearance. They ran year in and year out before needing any adjustments, always at the rate of three thousand revs per minute. When the day came to tighten up worn bearings, typical old-world craftsmanship was used. Without disturbing the spindle or bearing, the whole bearing area was enclosed in a ball of clay, the oil hole on top carefully kept open. A ladle of molten tin (previously heated on the smithy fire) was poured down the oil hole. Once cool and the clay removed, any previous play had vanished. Many of these machines were performing perfectly as late as 1940. On their base one would find the stamp 'Braithwaite. Crook, 1870'.

A turning machine spindle carried a heavy fly-wheel to keep the speed constant under their load. This fly-wheel was about ten inches in diameter, the rim being approximately two and a half inches, by two and a half. On one occasion, a machine had been built up and an extra large drum on the main shaft fed the belt down to the spindle. Nobody realized this spindle was going at almost three times the normal speed of three thousand revs. Harold Tyson was turning bobbins when the fly-wheel burst, missing his elbow by no more than an inch. Shrapnel sprayed up the far wall, through both slants of the roof and a large hunk was found in a garden at Lane Head, on top of the hill. It was a sobering experience.

Usually, if a machine was not in use, the belt was knocked off, that is the belt was removed from the big drum on the elevated shift. A light stick framework positioned between the drums, acted as a rest for the belt, preventing it from dropping onto the revolving shaft. Putting the belt back on again was a dangerous and un-nerving experience.

A narrow catwalk ran the full length of the shaft on the driving side, reached by an ordinary ladder from below. The worker knelt down and lifted the belt onto the nearest point of the rapidly revolving drum. Holding it with one hand, a small stick was inserted under the belt with the other. Slowly the stick pushed the belt over the arch of the drum to a point where it would grip and revolve. A cool head was crucial. The stick carrying the whirling belt was pushed further and further over the drum, until it finally slipped on unaided, leaving the operator on his knees hanging dangerously over the shaft.

Chapter Ten

The Machinery and Tools
of the Trade

Braithwaites – Tools and Toolmaking –
A Turner's Proud Possessions

Braithwaites of Crook were dominant in mill machinery from 1860 onwards. John Braithwaite was a mechanical genius without any formal training. It is said that he could not write his own name, but his inventions are certainly worth describing.

The Horizontal Boring Machine consisted of two spindles with bits engaging blocks which were fed on grooved rotating tables. The timing of each function was controlled by a system of cogwheels and cams and counter weights. The start and stop of all Braithwaite machines was achieved by pulling a single lever which tripped the driving belt from the idling pulley to the driving one.

The roughing machines had a basic similarity except that the driving spindles which spun the blocks were vertical. They too were fed with rotating tables, holding four points to support the rough blocks. Horizontal knives came in from the rear and planed the revolving wood down to size. This was simple ingenuity, no electrical circuitry or micro switches in those days. Provided the cutting edges were maintained, this type of machinery was perfectly trouble free and safe, especially in the hands of a youth. It was still in working order when it was finally destined for the scrap yard.

Braithwaite's Blocksawing Machine deserves a mention. It was a pedal-operated vertical drill adapted for use as a tubular saw. The operator held a slice of a log cut down to a pre-arranged thickness. It was then placed on a small support, the saw cutting out a block. On lifting the pedal the wood was moved slightly and the next block was cut. This procedure was continued until as many blocks as possible had been obtained and the waste that was left was in the form of a honeycomb. This curlicue waste was much in demand for firewood.

The redeeming feature of this machine was that it allowed the use of heavy timber and the liberty of working with green wood, which relieved us of the long period of natural seasoning.

Braithwaites were the chief supplier of bobbin mill machinery and tools in the area. This brochure dates from the 1950s. (Courtesy Eileen Thompson)

HENRY BRAITHWAITE & SONS

Mechanical Engineers

STAVELEY - WESTMORLAND

Makers of Tubular Saws   Bobbin Tools   Cork Cutters
Shell Boring Bits

Introducing Ourselves:

If you use our products, we need no introduction. However, we find that some of our customers are only acquainted with a small portion of our work, and we hope that you will find something new of interest.

Those who have not had the good fortune to use our products before, may be interested to know that a Braithwaite has been engaged in making woodworking tools and tubular saws for over ninety years. Thus we have a wealth of experience behind us. We need hardly add that despite our long experience, we are continually learning, and we find our tools, originally made purely for woodworking, being used for such modern materials as Perspex, and other plastics.

49

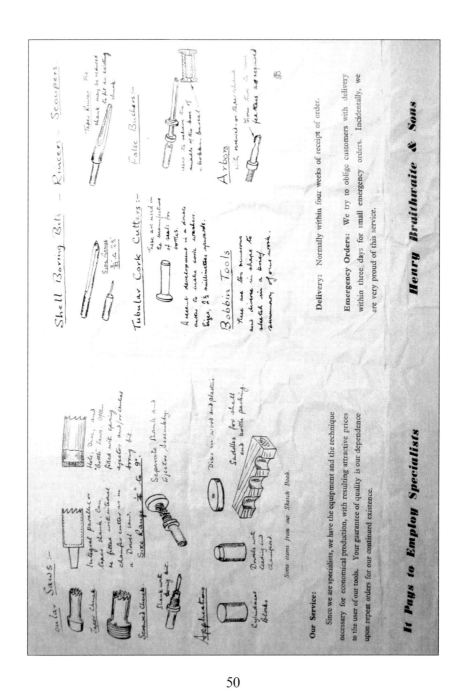

Some items from our Sketch Book.

Our Service:

Since we are specialists, we have the equipment and the technique necessary for economical production, with resulting attractive prices to the user of our tools. Your guarantee of quality is our dependence upon repeat orders for our continued existence.

Delivery: Normally within four weeks of receipt of order.

Emergency Orders: We try to oblige customers with delivery within three days for small emergency orders. Incidentally, we are very proud of this service.

It Pays to Employ Specialists

Henry Braithwaite & Sons

50

The blocksaw method was great for small sizes and huge quantities only. Anything beyond three inches long made it necessary to work it the 'coppice way'. After the blocks had been kilned and conditioned in the storage bins over the river, it was possible to bring them into the mill onto the automatic borers and then straight up to the turner. This method dispensed with slow hand boring and roughing. In essence, the blocksaw method was for volume in small bobbins, and the coppice for variety and larger sizes.

✕~◠~✕

The blacksmith's shop and mechanic's shop were on the left side of the yard. The forge and anvil and a collection of smithy tools were the simple equipment but here, for more than a hundred years, thousands of cutting tools had been fashioned to a wonderful degree of accuracy.

Let us trace the making of one tool.

A piece of steel would be cut off approximately eight inches long. Held by tongs the end was heated to a dull red and forged on the anvil to acquire a good profile. Next, it was roughly ground to get it more accurate and to achieve its first rough edge. Heated again (too hot would burn the metal), the tip was plunged into a pot of oil to chill the point but not the shank. A fast rub with a bit of limestone removed the soot from the surface, allowing one to watch the transfer of heat back to the tip in the form of a dull rainbow. The colours of value were light, medium and dark straw, through to middle blue. One seasoned worker remarked at the crucial moment, 'Lad, catch it like a pigeon's wing'. Anywhere from the very hard to soft was represented by this rainbow effect, necessitating a split second decision followed by a fast plunge into cold water.

The tool was ready to be ground on the big wet limestone wheel. Nobody ever managed this process without getting spattered with stone slurry. The edge was now without imperfections and ready to be whetted with a small hand stone. This process was done with the help of saliva, and a turner's mouth was always stained. The

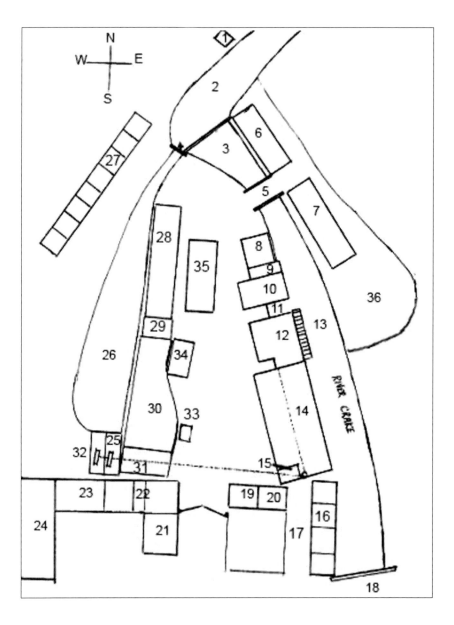

25 Plan and key (right) of Spark Bridge Mill (Douglas Philipson)

whetting appeared to be never ending for the turners were always after the ultimate and perfect edge. Finally the tool was fitted in the machine, its angle being absolutely crucial.

When these stages were completed, the tool cut like a razor, leaving a polished surface on the bobbin. Having reached this point of efficiency, this tool would be producing up to one hundred gross of bobbins per day. With as many as fifteen tools in a machine, requiring this exact care, it gives an indication of the degree of craftsmanship the men possessed. In nearly all cases the extent of their formal training did not go beyond the village school. From the grass roots up, they produced thousands of products in wood, consistently accurate, and they turned them out by the million. In all this they would fall back on the forge, the grindstone, the whetstone and their skill.

Tools and chisels were accumulated over a course of many years. They were a turner's proud possessions. Under each turning machine was a hollow space. A large swill stood on a small stool to catch the falling bobbins. Three sides were equipped with small shelves and a hessian curtain hung over the front. This was the turner's 'holy of holies. Nobody was allowed even to peek under there. Probably a younger man had inherited that lathe from an older employee. This developed into a fierce pride in possessions. Neatly laid out would be slippers, bevellers, gougers, toppers, edge tools, nibblers, end tools, profile tools and dozens of mandrels and tail pins. In many instances, a complete complement of tools, plus tin and paper packing were all carefully tied up with an original sample bobbin. The entire success of his performance hinged on control of this personal arsenal. If and when an old bobbin turner contemplated retiring, a murmur of excitement would develop among his colleagues as to the possibilities of getting a new store. Such was the respect developed over what would appear as mere detail to the laymen.

Chapter Eleven

Shavings and Sawdust

Shavings were the by-product of the bobbin industry. Each machine gave off its own particular type. There were frilly types, curlicues, wiry ones, and shavings ideal for packing china. There were small narrow ribbons and big long ribbons. Shavings eight inches wide and an eighth of an inch thick. Every tool produced a different type. The variety of this by-product never ceased to fascinate young and old.

To step into a bobbin mill on a day of rest was akin to stepping into a forest after a fall of snow. There wasn't a sound, the piles of clean shavings insulated and accentuated the silence. The myriad of belts hung from above like trees covered in dust. Benches and machines were covered with heaps of shavings and sawdust lay on every ledge. Feet ploughed underfoot like going through deep dry powder. An elbow catching a belt would bring down a fall of dust which stuck to one's clothes. In place of the pure air of the forest was the indescribable smell of fresh birch, newly released from millions of shavings.

Despite dust lying everywhere, the impression was one of cleanliness. The beautiful fresh cream of the shavings suggested a crisp winter scene. Heavy industries, like coal, steel and engineering have one thing in common, dirt and grime around their equipment – a hark back to the old phrase 'Where there's muck there's money'! Not so with bobbin making, the dust and shavings cleaned and polished everything. The smooth parts of machines were brightly polished and even castings adopted an appearance like a black-leaded grate. Wood meal, or dust, sapped up every particle of dirt and oil, indeed, only the main bearings showed signs of lubrication. Tool blocks or slides actually traversed on fine dust, their surfaces perfectly silvered and running without lubrication. Fine wood was a wonderful cleaning agent. Boots would polish automatically; clothes would cleanse themselves and remain clean. Never did a bobbin turner need to wash his hands. Tool handles, swill stands and stools were so polished over the years that it was sometimes difficult to prevent the swill from sliding off.

The mill floor was flagged, but seldom was it exposed. In the turning area it was similar to walking across a hay loft. Shavings are very springy, much like hay. Sawdust piled up in the blocking and sawing area. Borings and roughing tool shavings congested their respective machines.

Roughing machine shavings were the best for fuel, being thick and course. The boiler-man went for them first, and so did all the villagers. Despite the appetite of the boiler, sometimes the mill floor became choked. Turners would have to dig a hole for themselves to stand at their machines. Walking on the increased height brought heads into contact with the belts, a dangerous situation calling for swift action.

Sometimes labour would be assigned to work in the evenings. A farmer's fork was the ideal tool to pull apart heavily matted shavings. We loaded the wagon and ran the loads over the bridge to the 'black patch'. Load after load would be spread until the mill was empty. Only then would it be lit, often burning away for three days.

The villagers were allowed to fill a bag with shavings on the deposit of one halfpenny. This was no simple undertaking as the bag was usually the biggest and lightest there was. The most solid type of shaving was rammed in until the filled bag had the appearance of a compressed bale of hay. When not another flake could be crammed in, a string was wound across the top.

An old pensioner may have taken an hour to fill his bag and by then it was probably too heavy for him to lift. Sometimes a mill boy would leave his machine and dash up the valley with the bag if he could manage it, without the foreman seeing him.

The hollowing-out of wire bobbins gave off the best shavings. The 'sliper' or 'barrel tool' as it was known, would yield a perfect ribbon three inches wide and as much as 30 feet long. As each bobbin was turned, the shavings would fly over the shoulder of the operator and across the floor.

As kids we loved to catch the 'last one' and roll it up, never quite knowing what were going to do with it.

Chapter Twelve

The Boiler House, Dyeshop and Barrel House

The boiler was a monster. It was far too big to be kept going by shavings alone but the foreman, Alf Westall, would never allow any wood to be burnt. Firewood cost sixpence a bag; much too valuable to be consigned to the fire.

A lad would be given the unpopular job of stoker. He spent all day filling outsize sacks with shavings, humping them on to his back and tipping the contents into the stokehold or boiler hole, as it was known. The two fire tubes were fed with a common black iron shovel, but with so much use the boiler shovel looked as if it had been silver plated.

With a large draughty chimney a shaving fire did not last long. It was sheer slavery to feed those two fires, yet a hard working youth earning fourteen bob a week would manage to raise as much as ninety pounds of steam. This was an accomplishment most boilers would only attain by burning coal.

At night the boiler was banked up. The boy worked even harder during the last hour to preserve his steam overnight. A somewhat mysterious blend of sawdust and shavings was rammed in, and with pride he would be met with probably twenty pounds of steam still intact next morning. Every lad had his own formula for banking up.

Internal rust is the bane of all boilers and the problem was solved by tipping half a pail of ordinary washing soda from the village shop through the manhole cover every Monday morning. An annual inspection was carried out by the Board of Trade. The inspector always commented on the rust-free interior.

Two long flues running the length of the boiler each side, and going for yards to the bottom of the chimney, had to be cleaned of soot prior to inspection. Two lads would volunteer for the job because there would be a few extra bob in the pay packet. But a more miserable job one could not imagine. In complete darkness with only room to crawl through the seemingly endless flues, loads of soot were painstakingly extracted before the lads reappeared totally black from head to toe, sporting two white eyes! With the boiler cold and empty there was no hot water to be had. Their clothes had to be burned.

In those days the entire place could not boast a single bathroom with running water. The lads would make themselves as presentable as possible, and then bike to their homes where again there would be no bathroom. How nice to have the boiler going again the next day, giving off heat everywhere and providing steam and hot water.

<hr>

The dye shop sat between the kilns and the boiler house. It was a raised deck affair, half on land and half over the river edge supported on stilts. Square wooden tubs about two feet across and six feet deep held the liquid dye, a tub for each colour. Iron framed square cages covered with chicken wire were used to hold the bobbins for dying. The cage was moderately filled; a wooden lid and two cross pegs were fitted to control the load. Two lads grasped a handle on each side, hauled it up and then lowered it into the vat, dunking the whole load up and down for a strict three minutes before pulling it out.

An impending session at the dye tubs was greeted with growls and grumbles, especially from the boiler boy who would lose his precious head of steam. The process began with an unearthly scream of steam being fired into the tub to bring the cold dye to a boil. This took about twenty minutes and disaster reigned if the steam wasn't cut at boiling point. Froth and boiling dye would fly everywhere, a most unholy mess.

When the tubs were boiling and the bags of bobbins ready on the site, Alf Westall would take command. Six lads sitting on dry cosy jobs in the mill would be told to come and bring their empty swills. Into the tub went the cage, three minutes up and down and out, dye and foam dripping everywhere. Alf would bark 'Into the middle!' Water from two buckets would be thrown at the frothy cage, rebounding in all directions and wetting everyone's legs. 'More water!' and the bucket brigade obliged from the bed of the river, tipping water onto themselves as they handed it up to head height. By now, everywhere was awash. Assuming the cage was now clean of surplus dye and froth, Alf would order 'Tip them out!' The hot dripping cage was hoisted up by two lads who emptied the contents into the six swill baskets they straddled. 'Onto the kiln!' Alf would yell. Then we would dash up the stone steps with water cascading down our legs, tip out the bobbins, dash back and prepare for the second batch. This ritual was repeated until the job completed and the place had been swabbed down. Keeping dry was impossible and many a lad biked home in the dark with dye splattered and soaked trousers. On such occasions Alf Westall was not in our bedside prayers! It was an infinitely more pleasant task lifting bobbins off the warm kiln the next morning ready to go inside the barrels for smoothing and waxing.

✖══✖

The barrel house was a low structure adjacent to the end of the mill. Barrels were big drums with an axle through the middle to allow them to spin on bearings. They had a door on the outside and were driven by a slow moving belt around the perimeter. There were seven barrels which were used for different purposes, ranging in diameter from three to six feet.

Their function was two-fold, to riddle out all the shavings and sawdust from the bobbins and to smooth the product. In actuality, the shavings helped to polish the bobbins before they left the barrel. Slowly trundling around for two hours gave them a beautiful sheen. When the barrel was stopped and emptied the contents were tipped into swills. If the barrel was tipped even the slightest fraction too far, the highly polished bobbins would fly across the floor like marbles.

Many other finishes were achieved. Talc was used and dyed bobbins were polished with beeswax. A form of sanding was done by using powdered abrasives and a successful process of colour enamelling was achieved on articles such as smooth handles, wooden balls and beads.

One little-known process was burnishing. After the bobbins had been dyed and waxed in the tumbling barrel they were well polished, but the process was taken a step further. They were put through a half self-actor turning machine again but instead of a battery of sharp tools, they were met with a set of blunt tools, very like the ends of a spoon handle. There was a tool for each surface and the combination of friction on the waxy surface and the smooth steel produced a remarkably high gloss. Ash, a hard wood, was always used in this instance.

Chapter Thirteen

The Packing Loft

The Sorting Table – Quality Control – Bagging–
Cleaning the Hole – Despatch

When the bobbins were out of the barrels, they were carried in swills upstairs to what was known as the packing loft, a large spacious room with a slated roof coming down to the floor on both sides. The only daylight in the place came from skylights in the roof but it was quite adequate. Two huge barrels in the middle of the floor ran incessantly polishing the dyed bobbins. A long sloping table divided into three by partitions and boarded high on the back and sides, acted as sorting and counting tables. There was a low edge along the front with a gap in the centre which was covered by a removable stick. This allowed the work to trundle through into a swill below.

The sorting tables were used as a labour reservoir for youths moving between one machine job and another. What a bewildering task it was for young folk, surrounded by mountains of bobbins. A great sea of cream surfaces, some no larger than a small thimble, all to be expertly scrutinized for chips or flaws which could snag a cotton thread during the winding process. It took skill, concentration and an eagle eye, and still some defective ones got through.

Quality control is a highly sophisticated segment of modern industry, indeed today's manufacturing world would come to a halt without it. Scientific testing equipment, complex referral data – the aids to attaining quality in our factories today are endless. In the bobbin trade quality control was equally as important but it was

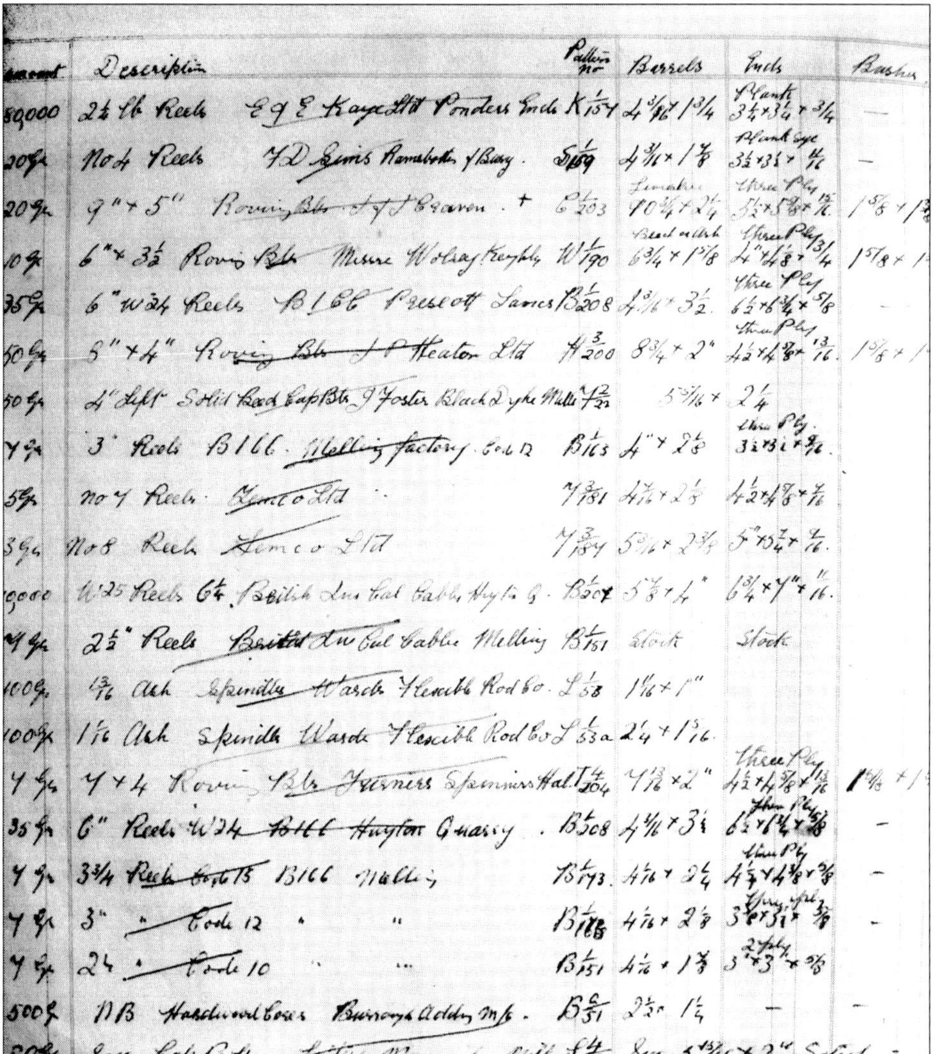

Amount	Description	Pattern No	Barrels	Ends	Bashes
80,000	2¼ lb Reels E & E Kaye Ltd Ponders End	K 1/157	4 3/16 × 1 3/4	Plank 3¼ × 3¼ × 3/4	—
20 gr	No 4 Reels J D Lewis Ramsbottom & Bury	S 1/159	4 3/16 × 1 7/8	Plank eye 3½ × 3½ × 4/16	—
20 gr	7" × 5" Roving Bts J & J Craven +	C 1/203	Laminated 10¾ × 2¼	Three Ply 5½ × 5 5/8 × 15/16	1 5/8 × 1 3/8
10 gr	6" × 3½ Roving Bts Messrs Wolsey Keighley	W 1/190	Bead & [illegible] 6¾ × 1 5/8	Three Ply 4" × 4 1/8 × 3/4	1 5/8 × 1
35 gr	6" W 24 Reels B I C C Prescott Lancs	B 1/208	4 3/16 × 3½	Three Ply 6½ × 6¾ × 5/8	—
50 gr	8" × 4" Roving Bts J & P Heaton Ltd	H 3/200	8¾ × 2"	Three Ply 4½ × 4 5/8 × 13/16	1 5/8 × 1
50 gr	4" Lift Solid Bead Cap Bts J Foster Black Dyke Mills	F 2/22	5 5/16 × 2¼		
7 gr	3" Reels B I C C Melling factory Code 12	B 1/163	4" × 2 1/8	Three Ply 3½ × 3½ × 9/16	
5 gr	No 7 Reels Lemco Ltd	7 3/181	4 7/16 × 2 1/8	4½ × 4 7/8 × 7/16	
3 gr	No 8 Reels Lemco Ltd	7 3/187	5 3/16 × 2 3/4	5" × 5¼ × 7/16	
9,000	W 25 Reels 6¼ British Ins Cal Cable Huyton Q.	B 1/207	5 7/8 × 4"	6¾ × 7" × 11/16	
4 gr	2½" Reels British Ins Cal Cable Melling	B 1/181	Stock	Stock	
100 gr	13/16 Ash Spindles Wards Flexible Rod Co.	L 1/58	1 1/16 × 1"		
100 gr	1 1/16 Ash Spindles Wards Flexible Rod Co	L 1/53a	2¼ × 1 3/16		
4 gr	7 × 4 Roving Bts Forners Spinners Hall	T 4/204	7 13/16 × 2"	Three Ply 4½ × 4 5/8 × 11/16	1 5/8 × 1
35 gr	6" Reels W 24 BICC Huyton Quarry	B 1/208	4 3/16 × 3¼	Three Ply 6½ × 6¾ × 5/8	—
7 gr	3¾ Reels Code 15 BICC Melling	B 1/173	4 7/16 × 2¼	Three Ply 4½ × 4 3/8 × 5/8	—
7 gr	3" " Code 12 " "	B 1/168	4 7/16 × 2 1/8	Three Ply 3½ × 3½ × 3/8	—
7 gr	2¼ " Code 10 " "	B 1/151	4 1/16 × 1 7/8	2 Ply 3" × 3" × 5/8	
500 gr	NB Hardwood Cones Burrows Adding M/c	B 6/51	2½ × 1¼	—	—
50 gr	Dye Cap Bts Listers Manningham Mills	L 4/23	Dye 5 13/16 × 2" Solid		—

A page from a 1950s order book

(Courtesy Eileen Thompson)

obtained by contrasting methods. The key worker was the turner who produced the final product. He was on piece work and he worked entirely for himself first and the company second. Anything defective arriving at his machine would produce a hostile outburst to the people below him in the chain.

The sawyer sometimes cut blocks with sloping ends rather than at right angles. This would show up on the bobbin, causing rejects. The term was known as 'sap whistled', alluding to the old rural practice of using a green stick to make a whistle with sloping ends. The sawyer was left in no doubt of his fellow worker's displeasure.

Holes in blocks had to fit a push gauge. Too slack, and the work would slip on the turner's mandrel. Too tight would mean he could not get the bobbin on. Woe betide the bit fettler! If the block was roughed too small the next man up would complain. The turner's dimensions had to be perfect, no tolerance was allowed. These men used no slide rules or micrometers or sophisticated means of measuring.

When a sample came from the customer, it was passed to the mechanic to make a gauge. This consisted of a piece of stout sheet iron about two by ten inches. Rectangles were cut around its perimeter to accommodate the dimensions and profiles of the bobbin. Every segment fitted into its own particular gap. That was all.

These simple methods, coupled with a pride in workmanship seemed to work miracles. Hundreds of products, possibly millions of pieces, were produced and very rarely was anything found wanting. Quality control existed but I cannot say that it was recognized as such. It was a rare day that a customer returned a bag of bobbins.

The sorting tables provided a welcome opportunity for the young to relax and gossip but we would always be on the lookout for Alf who could appear from nowhere to give us a verbal tirade – all the while rifling his hand through our sorted swillful and saying 'And here's another and another….' His ability to find defects in our already 'good' swill was humiliating

After sorting, the swillfull was loaded on to the counting table. The counting machine was a horizontal bar which hung from a beam. A small pan hung on one end and a larger one hung lower on the other with a sloped end for pouring. The ratio was twelve to one (we dealt in grosses). In about three minutes, it was possible to count six swillfulls of bobbins accurately into a large farmer's grain sack. Two people would take hold of the lug over the forearm, hoist together, and every crease would be out of the bag. A bobbin looped onto the bag with string would indicate the number of bobbins it contained. Large bobbins were counted by hand, actually in both hands; three in each hand counted as one, multiplied by twenty four equals a gross.

Now that the product had gone its full course, from the wood yard to the packing loft and into bags, there remained one last process – that of cleaning out the hole of any whiskers and correcting possible shrinkage. Cotton spinners could not tolerate variations on their spindles, hence the chore was left to last. It was considered an ideal job for a teenage boy; it proved to be a heart-breaker of monotony.

Three stumps of wood stood around a whirling bit, the centre one for the operator to sit on, and one each side of the bit to hold the full and the empty swills. The bit was similar to a boring bit, except the cutting edge was on the side and the point was blunt. We became adept at whipping the bobbins up the bit, down and off into the empty swill in a never ending process. The knots in the wood jammed the bobbin on the bit and burnt our fingers. This went on hour after hour and we went home in agony, only to return to it the next day. The small diameter bobbins were the worst to grip and sometimes a bag held as many as seventy gross.

We thought we would never get out of our misery and Alf would send us back to it if we ever plucked up enough courage to complain!

Finally, the bag was stitched with strong string and a packing needle. An ear was made at one end, the top being stitched with a lock stitch and finished off with the second ear. This was the only way to grip a full bag once it was closed.

Two trap doors in the floor opened up to reveal an area below, complete with hayricks, where the cart could back in. A much used and polished plank was the means of sliding the bags down to the cart. A full load of bobbins covered with a tarpaulin would trundle out of the yard like a load of hay, on its journey to Greenodd station. The return trip took about two hours.

Many a frantic morning was spent in that loft, getting everything ready for the cart. There were pressures and deadlines to be met, just as today. Bobbins were rushed upstairs from the barrel house and onto sorting tables, as many as four people sorting them frantically against time: Edith, who was in command of the bagging, giving orders to everyone else at the same time (this was her domain); the lads stitching the bag tops; a howl of 'That won't do. Pull it out again' when a bag appeared too slack to travel safely; 'Pattie', growling under the trap-door – 'Come on, the 'orse won't stand'. Finally, a check to make sure all the bags had their address labels.

Down the chute the whole lot went and the carter was finally on his way. The trap doors were closed, the surplus labour dismissed and relative peace returned until the next time.

Chapter Fourteen

Come into the Office

Comnnications – Wages – Piece Work – Pay Day –
Terms and Conditions of Employment – Alf's Little Book –
Health and Safety – The Can Lad

The nerve centre of any business has to be its office. Our office was built into the first accessible corner of the mill, as approached from the main entrance gates. Entered from outside, an inner door allowed one to step into the main mill. Along the inner wall was row of windows, allowing a view of the mill interior.

The desk was a huge double-sided affair with two sloping hinged lids covered in green leatherette and a rim at the bottom to prevent articles falling off. Across the raised centre was a book or ledger rack made entirely of polished turned spindles, as many as eight spindles supporting the rack. The ornate set with its fancy glass jars for blue and red ink, and the rack holding the nib pens were still there in the late thirties. Father was using the fountain pen by now. An exceptionally wide mahogany counting table rested along one wall. This sat on a stack of drawers and was really a stand up table. Needless to say, one wall was a mass of bobbin samples on nails and strings, etc. They hung like bunches of grapes. These were the current samples, thousands of others having been relegated to the archives.

Let into the deep mill wall by the door was the steel safe. This only ever carried 'the books'; the day book and the cash book, all kept up to date. There was a total absence of mechanical or electronic office equipment. Even pencils were sharpened with a penknife. A typewriter made its appearance eventually, but before that all letters were written by hand.

Not one penny was spent on advertising. Most of the principle cotton spinners were old respected businessmen, as were the bobbin manufacturers. When they needed bobbins, their order would automatically come in. Sales promotions and gimmicks would not have had the slightest effect. An agreed price on placement of order was the only pre-requisite. Any idea of a phone was considered the height of extravagance though such things were then in existence. The bobbin mill did occasionally receive phone calls but they always came through the village shop. Mrs Westall would rush down into the mill yard, frantically asking for my father. Her shop and customers would have to take this interruption in their stride. Telegrams were more popular than phone calls, but they too were delivered through the village shop. Britain, as a whole, seemed to come to the solid conclusion that this was the way to get action from rural Spark Bridge.

One aspect of life which could not be criticised however, was that a letter mailed anywhere in Britain during the previous evening would drop onto the office floor before seven thirty the next morning. Has there been any improvement?

In 1928 we still had the Empire and the old currency. Both are now gone. I am referring to the coinage carrying the head of George V. To change from the status of a school boy (with no visible means) was an exhilarating experience. A curt 'Start on Monday' was all that was said. A three-month period was served to see how the lad made out. All being well, he now received twelve bob. This was real money! Usually the yearly increment was two shillings. Presumably this covered the cost of living and also allowed for a boy moving into manhood.

Very soon after we started we noticed some fellows rushing about and working like fiends, they were even truculent if anything or anyone stopped them working. This was our first introduction to the piece work system, so much per gross instead of so much per hour. Tales abounded of the fabulous money to be made. We couldn't wait to get onto piece.

Many of the trouble-free processes lent themselves to piece work. Boring, roughing, dishing, cutting off ends, there were many such jobs. The prices per gross ran from three quarters of a penny, seven eighths of a penny and one and one eighth pence. Alf would tell us to start on piece and we'd dash up to the turner to find out the size of the order. Fast calculations, two hundred gross, multiplied by three quarters of a penny? We worked like demons and probably made an extra three and six or four bob at the end of two weeks. It was a great feeling to be rubbing shoulders with the Governor of the Bank of England!

The whole mill ran on a time and piece system, men swapping from one practice to the other intermittently. The administration to cover all this was contained in a grubby little note book in Alf Westall's pocket, mixed in with keys, whetstones etc. No man had a card and there was no time-clock. With a stub of pencil Alf would record the details and pass them on to the office every second week.

The first week's pay was a 'sub', the second was full pay, with much attention to detail being paid by all parties. Typically, a man might have four amounts of hourly work at the current rate, and four quantities at varying prices per gross. It was remarkable how the men calculated their wages so accurately.

The wage clerk had the job of working out each man's pay when the final counts came in from the packing room. Thursday night was 'close off' for figures coming into the office. A trip to town on Friday morning secured the right amount of cash from the bank and it was laid out on the counting table in suitable denominations. An old square tobacco box with a hinged lid was used to house each man's pay, his name being on the lid. The pay was counted into the boxes and if all went well not a penny was left. It was very easy to check the contents of an open box if there was an error. A simple-self checking system. A swill was placed outside the office window and having collected their wages the men threw their 'bacca' box back into it to be used again next time. The pay parade consisted of an unofficial pecking order, old timers first, the youngest boys last. After all his labours, if a man's calculations fully materialized in his

Page from an 1880 wages book. The calculations are complicated – a combination of time and piece working. (*Courtesy of the Philipson family*)

Payments Leger 1926. Note the payment to Thos Middleton for swills and the large bill paid to L M and S Railway for carriage. (*By kind permission of Eileen Thompson*) box he would ride home cheerfully on his bicycle and not even notice if it was raining.

From the humble ten shillings per week of a youth, the scale became three pounds or three pounds two shillings and sixpence for the skilled turner on full piece work. This was considered a good wage in its day and men managed to keep their wives and children though there were precious few luxuries. The odd glass of beer in the pub on Saturday night and summer evenings spent on their allotment gardens were the main diversions.

The last boy (and the youngest) to have the honour of getting his name on the payroll was dubbed 'the can lad' by all workers. A Mrs Dickinson lived in a cottage just outside the mill gates and she was contracted to supply hot water for the men's tea cans. The workers deposited their cans with her each morning, the loose tea and sugar already inside. Breakfast was between eight and eight-thirty, the mill bell being the undisputed signal. Many cans were aluminium, some were enamelled and some had handles. The cans were filled just before eight o'clock and placed on top of the water butt. If the old lady's clock didn't synchronise with the mill time, the cans would get cold, leaving everyone impatiently waiting and every moment counting. With the first peal of the bell the can boy dashed to do his duty, coming back with about twenty wire handles hanging off his fingers. Searching out the men in their different work places he had to be able to distinguish their individual cans and make the deliveries. Receiving much abuse on his way the poor boy wasn't allowed to settle to his own breakfast until the last man got his tea. Before the half hour was over he had to collect all the recharged cans (no swilling out) then deliver them to the water butt in readiness for the mid-day break. It was a thankless task with no relief in sight until some other unsuspecting youth decided bobbin making was going to be a life of paradise for him!

Fringe benefits were something never heard of in those days. One week's holiday was the usual rule. Few people would make plans to go away. Mostly they stayed at home doing the odd jobs that needed to be done around house. Not to have to go to work for one whole week was relief enough though many chose to work during the holiday, the extra money being a godsend.

During shut down, the pentrough had to be scraped and painted. Beams and wheels would be brushed down, boiler flues cleaned. Dirty work, but it meant a change of job and a few extra shillings. Men with families were keen to get the extra work. Statutory holidays with pay were unknown. It was nice to look forward to Easter or Whitsuntide, but it meant a short week.

Extra hours were not alluded to as overtime, and there was no such thing as time-and-a-half, or double-time. The term bonus didn't mean anything. Coffee breaks were unknown. A worker was allowed thirty minutes for breakfast at eight o'clock; this was a must in view of a six-thirty start. The mid-day break was at twelve-thirty. These were the only interruptions in the day. If a man continued working until late in the evening, he went from lunchtime until leaving for home without taking a break. Such conditions seem harsh but people seemed to take them in their stride.

Absenteeism was almost unknown and no personal records were kept. Simple logic prevailed – no work, no pay. Other than injury when working it was rare for anyone to be off. In those early days the worker went to his station when the bell tolled, there was no card to punch or book to sign. In short, people were only conspicuous when absent. Invariably a discreet tap on the office door by a fellow worker would explain his colleague's dilemma, and an urgent assurance that the missing person would be back as soon as possible. Only a mental record would be needed for the making up of pay.

Some years later I heard of a happy-go-lucky chap who started coming in to work late every morning. At this particular time we had a manager who lived in Grange, requiring a train to Ulverston where he was met by a car and chauffeur, to be driven six miles to Spark Bridge Mill by 9.30 am. Using his personal experience as a shining example, the boss suggested that surely the tardy worker could do equally as well. He was met with the retort: 'Aye, but thou ain't doin it for yan tuppence an hour.'

One day after the first few weeks of employment, three young lads and I were summoned to the office. Doctor Penny's touring car sat in the mill yard. The doctor was inside talking with my father. Having looked us over he commented, 'A fine lot of lads you have here Mr Philipson', whereupon we were dismissed. This was our sole medical inspection to allow us to go into the bobbin-making profession.

Many daily working practices were quite dangerous. The later mode of fencing off vulnerable areas being only in its infancy. Indeed, the whole Victorian operation would be outlawed by today's standards of safety. Many accidents did occur. The minor ones were swiftly dealt with and it was a case of 'back to work' and 'grin and bear it'.

A frequent problem was getting fine chips of wood in the eyes, sometimes nothing bigger than a grain of sand. A worker would approach another with an index finger on his cheek. It meant he needed a particle removed from his eye. Often it was too noisy to ask what had happened. A ribbon shaving about two inches wide, was chosen and fractured in such a way as to produce a fine wooden bristle. The end was chewed until it was quite soft and pliable and the offending particle would be removed from the eye. A simple but effective remedy. This ritual was often used if two people had a parcel of gossip to exchange!

Now and then a serious mishap would incapacitate a person. After a visit to the village doctor, he would have to stay off work. Again no pay, but after three days a few shillings would be paid by the National Health. This service was handled by the big insurance companies through their local agents. Even so, an injured man had a habit of showing up at the 'scene of the crime' while on convalescence.

A black box in the office carried the medical supplies. A worker by the name of Jimmy Edwards, a turner, had passed the St Johns Ambulance Course. Jimmy rose to his full importance when called upon. On receipt of a frantic call for help, he would go into the most elaborate ritual of removing every trace of dust and shavings from his person. This infuriated everyone and there were cries that the victim was 'bleeding to death'.

In the earlier stages of the industry, working conditions were truly severe. Men and boys worked appallingly long hours, often seeing daylight only on Sundays. Reports say they were white faced and very unhealthy, the result of dusty conditions, no sunlight and a stodgy diet of carried food, with tea the only drink available.

My grandfather, William Philipson, along with many other manufacturers, unashamedly campaigned to wean boys away from any form of education, and he put them straight into the mill as soon as they were able to do lighter jobs. He believed 'book learning' to be a waste of time. Two boys provided back up for a turner, surely a perfectly good use of human resources. However, pressure was finally brought to bear by local authorities, resulting in a ruling whereby boys would go to school for half the day and the remainder would be spent at work in the mill.

I was fortunate to have a conversation with the last Mr Walker, of Force Forge, just before he died. Walkers had been bobbin manufacturers for many years. He told me how in the early days they employed indentured apprentices. Young boys, sent from the workhouse, lived in a loft above the machines and were fed by their employer. It was a brutal existence, the stuff of a novel by Charles Dickens.

Chapter Fifteen

Assorted Tales

'The Bobbin Mill Fliver' – Lighting the Lamps –
Getting to Work – Work Attire

Around 1935 the decision was made to modernise our transport depot. With the help of Hugh Leck (builder of Backbarrow) we acquired an old brass fronted, bull nose Morris Cowley touring car. Leaving the windscreen intact, the rest of the body was stripped away. A square box-like cab was fitted and the rear area was boarded to take about twelve sacks of bobbins. It was immediately dubbed the 'Bobbin Mill Fliver', with me doing most of the flying about. Three return trips to Greenodd station in sixty minutes was one of my foolish youthful accomplishments. In those days there was a notorious narrow bottleneck at the rear of Penny Bridge Hall, flanked by high walls on both sides. Racing through the neck one morning, I skimmed the side of the Coniston bus and the high garden wall. The bus driver was white with rage and when he jumped down I panicked and drove on, waiting for the police to catch up with me later. No repercussions! Alas, youth and discretion did not go together.

Prior to this modernization, our only means of acquiring anything from Ulverston was by carrier. A man called John Jackson operated a carrier service between Ulverston and Coniston, taking instructions on the way down one day, and returning on Thursday which was market day. His brother Aaron ran the Hawkshead carrier service. They also provided a comprehensive news service and many a night they were somewhat late in getting home.

75

After dark the mill was lit by paraffin oil lamps which were hung over the machines on long wires from the roof. They were strictly utility, a small reservoir and burner covered by a large ring and funnel-type shade to direct the light onto the job. The signal to muster the lamp parade came from Alf who would light his own lamp and swing it backwards and forwards, like the proverbial 'holy man'! Once the chimneys had been polished with small shavings the lamps were lit. Their mellow beams cast light onto the polished machinery, leaving the remainder of the mill in pronounced shadow. By modern standards it was not the most efficient way of lighting, but the overall effect was quite remarkable, a mixture of cosiness and warmth.

The combination of shavings and oil lamps was hazardous. A lamp which hadn't been used for a while would gather a heavy coat of dust, and eventually this would become impregnated with paraffin oil. Sometimes a lad would skip the oil parade and the cleaning process and just light up. Once the lamp warmed the oily dust would ignite. One scream would bring a rugby scrum into action. Lamp, chimney and all would be thrust into a shaving heap with a bunch of bodies sprawled on top. There wasn't a moment to look for water or a fire extinguisher. The lamp was extinguished. To cause a fire was about the greatest crime one could commit.

In 1928 it was rare for anybody to come to work in a car, not even the boss. About ten per cent walked, being lucky enough to live in the village. The rest came on bicycles, most of them of the old bone-shaker variety. A few came from Lowick, some from Colton and the village of Oxenpark. One or two came from Haverthwaite, and quite a few from Bouth. Ulverston produced the odd worker and there was one chap from Swarthmoor.

They all had one thing in common – the ability to negotiate hilly, twisting roads in all weathers and in the darkness of winter. Most would be on their way just after six-o'clock in the morning, allowing time to be there for the six-thirty start. Equipped with a 'tommy box' – the day's food – and tea can strung over the shoulder, one at the front and one behind, the cyclist's vital accessory was the paraffin oil bicycle lamp. On a black windy morning it was the last word in frustration.

John Jackson, carrier from Water Yeat, Blawith. He was one of many carriers who worked out of the towns of Ulverston, Keswick, Penrith and elsewhere. They delivered all manner of goods as well as providing a local news service.
(Courtesy of Irvine Hunt)

Three perils beset it: the flame rose too high and set the lamp on fire, the wind would blow it out, or the fancy oscillating double spring likewise would put it out. The lads would go whizzing downhill along twisting roads, at full speed in total darkness, when their feeble light would fail. More than one collision occurred, resulting in buckled wheels, bruised limbs and bad tempers for the rest of the day.

Arriving at the mill the men pushed their bicycle into woodsheds and any odd corner; each had his own private spot. Topcoat, box and can hung on a protruding coppice pole. If the man was soaked through he put his topcoat on the kiln, but his trousers would have to dry on him as he worked.

The typical youth going into the bobbin trade in those days was invariably a local lad; a cheap bicycle enabling him to cover the few miles between home and work. He wore heavy boots or clogs, a pair of corduroy trousers and a brown denim jacket known as a 'kitle' buttoning up to the neck, with no collar. The inevitable tweed cap with 'flipe' completed the picture.

Chapter Sixteen

Swills and Sacks

A swill was the main means of internal porterage. The floor was too congested to contemplate any form of wheeled truck. Departments were spread out and on different levels, making it necessary to have some form of hand-carrying apparatus. Primitive as it may appear, the humble swill gave complete satisfaction at every stage. That, coupled with the hessian sack.

The locally-made swill basket, measuring approximately 28 inches by 18 inches, was made of oak strips fastened to an oval frame shaped rather like the bowl of a spoon. Light in weight, it was hooked over the shoulder for carrying when empty. Everyone zealously guarded their swills and there was many a fight over their possession. Swills wore out in time and nobody wanted to be stuck with the 'holey' ones.

Between each process the bobbins were dropped into a swill, and when full, the contents were transferred to a sack. A fair amount of skill was needed to accomplish this if some of the contents were not to spill. The loaded swill was placed length-wise on the thighs, with one's body in a crouching position. The bag was partially pulled over the end of the swill and a series of jerks manoeuvred the load into the sack. The technique had to be varied as more swillfulls went into the bag. By the fifth and sixth swill load the bag was full to chest height. Similarly, emptying full sacks into the swills needed care. The

Middleton's swill making workshop at Mill Stile, Spark Bridge, c. 1900
(Courtesy of Irvine Hunt)

swill was placed at the right distance from the bag. The full bag was tipped over, its load falling exactly into the swill. Arms around the neck of the bag closed off the feed at the exact moment. The slightest miscalculation resulted in the bobbins spilled in all directions.

If the swill was the universal means of moving stock around the mill, then the sack was the only means of containing and shipping the finished product. The sack was ideal, cheap, light, and portable and it held its contents well once the top was stitched. With an address tally attached a bag was ready for dispatch and would stand being thrown about like a bale of hay. Rarely was damage caused in transit.

Thousands of bags and sacks were used annually. Sack dealers would scour the entire rural area, buying them from farmers before coming in with a full load to the mill. Sacks came in all sizes, all welcome for our trade. Before being stored in the sack loft, they all had to be turned inside out and shaken vigorously to remove particles of animal feed stuffs. Failing to do this would cause them to be riddled with rat holes and rendered useless. Being a cheap and efficient means of packing, few customers bothered to send them back.

Chapter Seventeen

Spark Bridge Village

Cottage Life – Village Folk – Allotments
– Trips to Ulverston

Several cottages lay adjacent to the mill. Two were up the yard, between the kiln and the wood yard, totally on enclosed land with the gates always closed at weekends. A strange environment for family life. An eccentric lady called Mrs Anderson lived in one cottage. When she papered the parlour she papered around the clock on the wall!

Three cottages faced the village green at the entrance to the mill. One housed the carter and his family, and the middle one was used for mill stores, every room holding different supplies. At a right angle and along the river edge were four more cottages. This was known as 'the alley' and I was told that years ago it had been referred to as 'Cock Alley'.

The focal point of these cottages, which included an outside corner of the mill, was a narrow neck where the village pump was situated. This pump had a partition across, necessitating two pump handles and a trough which pivoted so you could tip it either way. This was the hub of village life.

Cottage rents prevailing in 1928 varied. The bottom cottage had a rent of nine-pence; the second, one shilling and three-pence; the third two shillings and three-pence; and the top cottage four shillings.

The properties were old and draughty. Doors were ill-fitting and windows small. The cottages which stood against the river had only

A 1930's view of the mill complex and Spark Bridge village
(Courtesy of the Philipson family)

one door, with two steps down into the one-and-only room, with a 'back spot' behind. A black cooking range was the only means of cooking and heating, nevertheless some superb meals emerged from these primitive dwellings. It would be the task of the pensioners to sprinkle the shavings on the fire consistently, so that the 'old lady' could get her baking done. The women would swear that no other fuel could compare with the mill shavings for good baking.

Homes had no electricity, gas, hot or cold water, nor a bathroom or drains. The outside dry toilet at the bottom of the alley was the only sanitary arrangement.

An old turner became ill and died. No rent had been paid for more than two years but it was conveniently forgotten. The rents may have been small, but the comforts appear to have been even smaller. There was no magic or significance of the age of 'sixty-five', no suggestion or pressure on a person to retire. There was no company pension. The prospect of an old person sent home without means was unthinkable, and there was no question of asking him to go before his time.

A view of Spark Bridge workers' cottages looking over the roofs of the coppice barns and bobbin mill dam (Courtesy of the Philipson family)

Bernard Woodburn was a young, married man who lived in the bottom cottage in Cock Alley. He stood six feet in height, and was always in demand when strength was required. Alf wouldn't embark on any lifting job without a 'Where's Bernard? An excitable chap, he had a habit of adulterating his words with colourful language. 'Abso-flaming-bloody-lutely!' was one of his favourites. I remember him once describing a man he had seen going up the hill as having a sheet of 'congregational' tin on his shoulder!

Bernard wore his flat hat resting in the nape of his neck with the peak pointing upwards. When he became excited he would scratch the back of his head with the peak. I remember his first child being born. Someone looked in at the mill to ask Bernard to go home. He was sawing at the other end when the message was relayed. Within twenty minutes he reappeared to a chorus of 'What is it Bernard, a kettle or a pot?' Laughing and scratching his head with his hat, he replied 'Nay, it's nobbut a pot', and so saying, grabbed the next stick of wood and got back to work.

Spark Bridge. Looking down the mill race from the weir and sluice
(*Courtesy Eileen Thompson*)

A view of the River Crake with the mill yard on the left and two wood sheds on the right (*Courtesy Eileen Thompson*)

One day, a motorized fire pump was obtained and some of us got hold of the hose while it shot a full bore of water. Most of us aimed the stream as far as possible up the race. Bernard shot the water up into the air. We encouraged him to send it as high as he could. Everyone hastily backed off as we watched the downpour drench the fireman.

Jim Pattinson's cottage door was within a few yards of the office. His wife, Ruth-Anne, was a shy retiring person, and a fine character. She fed her hens twice a day, and made a point of keeping herself to herself. Originally a farmer's daughter, she was an excellent house-keeper and a superb cook. She insisted on giving me a mug of tea every morning and a piece of baking to go along with it. Eventually, with much protest, she agreed to accept payment of sixpence per week.

I remember an old woman called Maggie Jackson who lived in a tumbledown stone cottage, little better than a hovel. It sat on a rise above the village, commanding the finest view in the district. Her heap of stones is now long gone and a modern house stands on the site. Maggie was a recluse, and would have truck with no one. She kept a few hens and a kitchen garden, and sat with a candle after dark. She was a hard worker and a great walker. She would trudge the six miles to Ulverston every market day, humping a heavy produce basket while muttering away to herself; usually cursing the many people who felt compelled to slow down and offer her a lift. She always refused. Poor Maggie has been laid to rest for many years.

A fine character was Granny Burrow, who for many years ran the Royal Oak Pub in Spark Bridge, later passing it on to her daughter Cissie. The old lady went well into her eighties; her back bent, probably with rheumatics. She would come down the village to get a huge horse out of a field, her tiny frame leading it home. Next, one would see her mounted in an oversized two-wheeled float and she would be off to town at a brisk trot. She'd be back in the afternoon, 'loosing out' and taking the horse back to pasture. She was a fine old lady.

Her daughter, Cissie, was of the same resolute stock. She was a mature person possessing a rich voice, tinged with the Lakeland dialect. I remember being in the pub while she was reminiscing about her departed husband. They had been a devoted couple. With obvious emotion she explained how she dashed into Ulverston the day he died and bought the best white wool that money could buy and sat up all night knitting a pair of socks. She was determined his feet would be comfortable in his coffin.

Once, with her elbows on the bar, Cissie was elaborating on the joys of life. She said one of her greatest satisfactions was to lie in bed in fresh sheets dried in the wind that day, with a fire in the bedroom casting shadows on the ceiling and listening to the rain gurgling in the gutter under the eve. Cissie was a wonderful countrywoman who appreciated simple things.

The yard was always open to anyone who wanted sawdust, firewood or shavings. Farmers often came for the latter to be used as bedding for their cattle. We saw some real characters down from the fells, often on a soaking day, when 'thar was nowt doin' round't farm'.

The allotment gardens, situated beyond the village institute, seemed to be the main diversion from work. It was pleasant to tend a garden after so many hours indoors and the returns were most welcome. The main crop was potatoes, the seed being kept from the previous year. The wives would buy a score each of seedling cabbage and brussels sprout plants from the travelling greengrocer's cart.

The men seldom went to town but when a bus service started the womenfolk gradually got into the habit of going to market day in Ulverston. They would gather on the green, well before the bus was due, it being something of a social occasion. Once the bus was sighted flying down the hill into the village, Mary Walker, a some-what excitable lady, would make one last dash to her cottage door to make doubly sure it was locked properly, then arrive back at the bus out of breath when everybody was seated, almost unable to tell the bus driver of her intended destination. This happened every time she went on the bus, much to everyone's amusement.

Prior to the 1939–1945 war, change was taking place everywhere. The traditional worker – the man who had been content to work his life away, his pleasures consisting of an evening walk down to his garden – was dying off. The hours at the mill were being shortened and there was much more emphasis on the Saturday, looked on as a short day, with an early finish. There was now the solid prospect of 'doing something' or 'going somewhere'. Motor bus excursions were becoming popular; it was possible to go a greater distance from the village, within a short space of time, a situation hitherto undreamed of by the older generation only a few years before. The small compact car was selling to the select few for little more than one hundred pounds, though it was only a dream for the working classes. However, many workers were just able to finance a motor cycle, and in many instances, this proved to be the collateral which enabled the first workers to acquire a small car, possibly only a second-hand one. The old, cloistered way of village life had now gone.

Chapter Eighteen

More Mill Workers and a Tragedy

A chap called Frank Walker was a fairly typical mill worker in those bygone days. Standing around one day after my initiation, I felt a hand grasp my shoulder and a voice said 'Eh lad, I've worked for thee grenfether more'n fifty 'ear.' Frank was then sixty-five or more, a man of moderate height who wore mutton chop whiskers and an old bowler hat, which was on its way to a green tinge! His dialect was strong and he spoke quickly so I had difficulty in understanding him, having recently left Birmingham where I was raised. He had a remarkable, rolling walk, like an old sailor, and I often wondered if it had been caused by standing on shavings all his life. His eyesight was failing and he worked with steel-rimmed spectacles, which hung well down his nose. At the end of the day he would waddle through the mill door, up the Alley and into the second cottage. He had lived there for many, long years with his wife and grown-up daughter.

In his latter years Frank always seemed to be on the same machine. He turned all the big wire bobbins, the ones that spewed out the large chunky shavings that were so good for the fire. His fire was always fed by shavings; the coal man never called.

The years slipped by and Frank's eyesight became worse, though it was never mentioned. His ability to grind and hone and set his tools was remarkable and he continued to work with great accuracy. But old age caught up and he became very slow and went almost blind. He could still produce a good bobbin though his output became less and less and he made excuses as to why he hadn't done quite so many as yesterday.

After a period of intermittent absenteeism, he finally didn't come in. He hadn't quit – 'He'd be back in a day or two' – or so his wife said. But he didn't return. The next we heard was that the doctor was attending Frank for an infected foot, and soon he died. The fine old man must have been well into his seventies before he laid down his tools.

Jim Pattinson, the carter was a morose man. A smile was to be avoided at all cost. He didn't 'hold with the likes of...' Once his wife plucked up courage to ask why he never praised her cooking. He replied 'A'll tell thee when out's wrong!' Fine weather would see Jim set off to the station with his load, wearing a soft flat hat and his clay pipe upright. Wet weather produced an old 'billycock' hat, the brim turned down and his clay pipe inverted. A heavy sack round his shoulders completed the picture.

Soon after I'd started as a 'shiver' I arrived one morning at the entrance to the finishing department. It was 6.30 and I stood waiting in the dark for Edith Dickinson who was in charge of this end of the operation. She lived in the top cottage in the Alley, the only girl among a host of brothers. Coming in at the top door, she marched down the mill in the darkness, her clogs ringing on the stone floor. A beret totally covered her hair, black stockings and hessian apron completed the picture. Her philosophy was 'business and no nonsense'. She could more than hold her own with the mill men and the youths and generally ran a tight ship. A typical instruction would run: 'Nar then, young fella-me-lad, get them one ounces out of number five barrel on't first table, and mind thee picks'em all up'. A competent worker, she did wonders to get the loads ready for delivery.

Jim Casson was a little fat man with a jovial face, like a ripe straw-berry, topped off with a pork-pie hat. He was lame and walked with a hefty stick. He was one of three brothers who were all builders and dry-stone wallers. Jim has left some beautiful stone work around the

Village shop. This fragile, crumpled photograph was probably taken in the 1960s. Tommy Coward, on the left, a well-known village character, is chatting to Ethel Briggs (Courtesy Eileen Thompson)

mill site. Wood shed pillars were renovated, and some fine walls line the banks of the river to this day, all built in Lakeland cut stone. On finishing each night he would tip a spoonful of linseed oil onto his careworn grimy hands. He swore no chemist shop had any better cure. He would trudge home to Lowick Bridge, a long way for a man whose legs were not his greatest asset. Beneath his bluff exterior lay the nature of a very pleasant man.

An old rusty lady's bicycle, the sit up and beg type, vintage model, was ridden by a chap called Mark Barker. He lived on the main road at Crossamoor, which was well on the way to Dalton. I remember him as a man of about sixty. He had a thin frame and a thinner nose which always had a condensation problem! His shoes seemed to be falling off his feet and often they were wet through, but no one ever heard him complain. Mark's caustic wit and dry humour could almost be lit by a match. He would hold forth on various subjects, much to our amusement, tobacco juice flying into the nearest sawdust heap.

One day it was cats, the domestic variety. 'Thaa-sands of 'em howlin', can't sleep a wink at night, damn varmints!' His cure was to buy a pennyworth of hot potato chips, scatter them on the main Barrow road outside his house at night and rub them into the tarmac with his foot. The poor cat, engrossed in retrieving its late tasty supper was disposed of by heavy night traffic. Old Mark purred like a kitten, devilishly recounting how he had reduced the cat population.

Miles Burrows was a soft spoken, gentle man, his huge frame disguising a warm and tender nature. He did a lot of haulage for the local woodcutters and often came into the mill to get his loads weighed on the only scale in the district. Besides many loads of bobbin wood he would carry peeled oak for rustic work or for the swill makers; loads of birch besoms, oak bark for tanning leather, and bundles of hazel rods used as ships' fenders on docksides. Many products came from the coppice woods in those days.

Joe Williamson, always known as 'Firpo', was a tiny bantam of a man with a huge family. He was a builder's labourer and came to the mill occasionally when restoration work was being done. Joe was always ready to oblige with a convincing tall tale, told in the most serious manner. One particular day was no exception. On his bone-shaker bicycle, he had ridden from Greenodd to Keswick. Nothing exceptional about that but on the way back he lost the chain off his bike, and coming down Dunmail Raise his brakes failed and he began careering down at an alarming speed. Not to worry though! With split-second timing at the bottom of the hill, he turned right and hurtled on his way to Grasmere, so averting a tricky situation. Joe was only small but he knew how to reach his audience!

Our foreman, Alf Westall never smoked and my father, a heavy smoker, would often bait Alf to take it up. One day, with one foot out of the office door, Alf replied in his most ecclesiastical manner 'Mr Philipson, if the good Lord had intended us to smoke, he would have arranged to have a hole in the top of our heads!' The subject was never broached again.

One day in 1935 disaster struck. Alf was working on his beloved machine in the centre of the mill, directly under the main shaft. A bearing above his head overheated and caught fire. He shouted to someone to go and turn off the water, to stop the mill, a process which would take three minutes. The frustration must have been too much for him. He suffered a heart attack and died by his machine. My father and I, and all the workers and villagers, were shocked to the core. Everything came to a standstill and the wheels of the mill ceased turning until Alf was laid to rest.

Chapter Nineteen

The End of an Era

Looking back, I feel privileged to have had a glimpse of the way past generations lived and worked. All the modernization we take for granted today was nonexistent then: no electricity, washers, dryers or refrigerators. The list is long. Cars were in their infancy and television a recent invention. Bobbin mill owners were a stout breed of people. Their efforts and achievements were individual, not the result of a multi-national corporation. They looked after their own affairs with resolute determination. Not for them the world of credit and easy payments.

Although conditions were austere for owner and worker alike a mutual respect existed. There was a loyalty between workers and mill owners and the boss would see that his employees were treated fairly. Once national benefits began to appear this parental relationship gradually disappeared.

In almost every case the bobbin worker was of country stock, with an education not going beyond the village school. He or she would enter the mill at an early age and become proficient in the different processes of bobbin making, in most cases working up to becoming skilled in their craft. Their achievements were remarkable. They produced a wide range of products in great volume and accuracy, with few resources to draw upon. In 1928 Spark Bridge Mill employed approximately 60 people, with everyone contributing to the production process. In today's industry at least a third of those people would be checkers, quality controllers or planners. When tools and parts were found wanting they were fabricated on the premises. The blacksmith's shop was the birthplace for most innovations and modifications. Tools were made there that cut like razors. Craftsmanship was critical and the approach uncomplicated: either it was 'reight' or it was 'wrang'!

As the decade of the Twenties progressed, the medium-volume orders for bobbins and tassels were slowly diminishing. The Thirties was to see this situation reversed by the demand for toy parts, and a general variety of work occupying the machines. This new trade taxed the ingenuity of the establishment, calling for new equipment and skills.

But slowly the old Braithwaite machines were coming to a stop. Not because they were old and done. They were performing as lively as ever but sadly the trade was passing them by. The thousands of slippers, gauges and bevellers stacked under the machines, a collection of well over a century, were beginning to gather dust and get forgotten. The trend was universal. One by one the mills closed down.

The ten years immediately following the Second World War was to see the most remarkable revitalization of this sleepy old business when existing mills began pursuing a new trade in mill bobbins for the electronic wire trade. Starting from scratch, new techniques were mastered and the Spark Bridge Mill quickly gained the reputation for a first class product. The new built up type of bobbins were for fine wire for the electronic trade and demanded extreme accuracy. This business came under new management, but that is another story.

Towards the end of the war, after one hundred and fifty years of continuous working, the era of the humble wooden sewing cotton bobbin came to an end. This too, was the final curtain for a family which had devoted so much to the trade, spanning four generations.

>≈≈≈≈<

Douglas Philipson visiting Spark Bridge, 1985
(Courtesy of the Philipson family)

Index

97